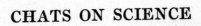

CHATS ON SCIENCE

THE DARK HORSE NEBULA IN ORION

A small region of the sky close to the easternmost star in the belt of Orion, photographed with the 100-inch Hooker telescope of the Mount Wilson Observatory of the Carnegie Institution of Washington. The white dots are stars, none of them bright enough to be seen with the unaided eye. Large dots are comparatively bright stars, while the tiny points richly scattered over the upper half of the picture are very faint stars requiring long exposures of the photographic plate to show them at all. The cloudlike mass in the lower half is probably just what it seems to be—a vast cloud of nebulous material, luminous in its upper portion, with a dark projecting mass in the center, outlined against the brighter background. The large irregular patch in the lower left corner is a star shining through and illuminating portions of the cloud and, like the sun shining through a cloud in our own atmosphere, is reddish in color. Few faint stars appear in the lower part of the picture, because most of these are very distant and are hidden behind the cloud. The nebula itself is so far away that five or six hundred years are required for its light, traveling at the rate of 186,000 miles per second, to traverse the distance separating it from the earth.

CHATS ON SCIENCE

BY

EDWIN E. SLOSSON, Ph.D.

DIRECTOR OF SCIENCE SERVICE, WASHINGTON; AUTHOR OF "CREATIVE
CHEMISTRY," "EASY LESSONS IN EINSTEIN," "MAJOR PROPHETS
OF TO-DAY," "SIX MAJOR PROPHETS"; CO-AUTHOR OF
"PLOTS AND PERSONALITIES," ETC.

ILLUSTRATED

THE CENTURY CO.
NEW YORK & LONDON

Printed in U. S. A.

CONTENTS

NUMBER		PAGE
1	THE CHATTABILITY OF SCIENCE	3
2	THE NEW WORLD	5
3	THE SINGING CRYSTAL	8
4	THE LIONESS AND THE HARE	12
5	THE SUPER-RATS	13
6	SCIENCE BEGINS IN WONDER	17
7	LET US LEAVE OFF LIVING ON LEAVINGS	20
8	ANCESTRAL SCANDALS OF SCIENCE	23
9	NATURE'S ADVERTISING	26
10	A CRAZY EXPERIMENT AND WHAT CAME OF IT	28
11	EINSTEIN IN WORDS OF ONE SYLLABLE	31
12	PERFUMES FROM POISON GAS	34
13	FRANKLIN'S FORESIGHT	38
14	EARLY BIRDS	41
15	A DANGEROUS MENTAL MALADY	44
16	THE SILKWORM'S RIVAL	48
17	HOW SCIENTIFIC INSPIRATION COMES	51
18	THE WAR OF LAND AND SEA	58
19	SCIENTIFIC FACTORS IN HISTORY	62
20	DO TWO AND TWO MAKE FOUR?	66
21	AN INVENTORY OF ENERGY	71
22	THE FIGHT FOR THE FOOD AND FUEL OF THE FUTURE	75
23	YELLOW JOURNAL SCIENCE	78
24	BYRON'S BLUNDERS	82
25	THE POPOVER STARS	84
26	SODA-WATER	90

viii   CONTENTS

NUMBER   PAGE

27 THE CULTIVATION OF OBLIVIOUSNESS 96

28 HOW A CHEMIST TRICKED HIS WIFE 98

29 WHAT IS THE MATTER WITH THE ARTISTS? 100

30 HOW MAN GOT HIS SHOE 102

31 SUMMER DRINKS 106

32 THE SUN-CURE 110

33 THE SCIENCE OF KEEPING COOL 114

34 WOMEN AS CHEMISTS 117

35 THE ADVANTAGE OF TAN 119

36 FROM COMPLEXES TO GLANDS 122

37 GEOLOGISTS GET AN EXTENSION OF TIME 125

38 HOW OLD IS DISEASE? 127

39 HAS SCIENCE REACHED ITS LIMIT? 130

40 HOW THE OTHER HALF OF THE PLANT LIVES . . . 132

41 PERCENTAGE ALIVENESS 135

42 MAKING SUNSHINE FATAL 138

43 GASOLENE AND ALCOHOL 141

44 THE FIGHT AGAINST THE POTATO 143

45 OUR DOMESTIC ENEMIES 145

46 DO THE PAPERS LIE ABOUT SCIENCE? 149

47 GIVE US SHORT NAMES 151

48 THE INEFFICIENCY OF AGRICULTURE 153

49 THE BODY-GUARD 155

50 EINSTEIN'S CREASE 157

51 THE SUCCESS OF A FAILURE 162

52 IRON NERVES 164

53 SCIENCE FROM THE SIDE-LINES 168

54 IN DEFENSE OF FIREPLACES 170

55 THE SOCIAL PSYCHOLOGIST IS COMING 173

56 HOW WORDS LOSE REPUTATION 175

57 HIGHWAYS OF KNOWLEDGE 178

CONTENTS

NUMBER		PAGE
58	MAN AND THE MACHINE	180
59	SHARK-TOWED SUBMARINES	184
60	MAN AFRAID OF NOTHING	186
61	MIND-CLEANING TIME	189
62	NEW LIGHT ON THE ORIGIN OF LIFE	191
63	MAKING MEDICINES HIT THE MARK	195
64	HOW THE CHEMIST MOVES THE WORLD	199
65	TO EXCHANGE: A CHEMIST FOR A COLONY	201
66	THE ECLIPSE AND EINSTEIN	204
67	THE FAITH OF THE SCIENTIST	208
68	THE TERRITORIAL WARS OF BIRDS	211
69	FARADAY'S RAZORS	214
70	BACK OF BABEL	216
71	HOME-MADE RUBBER	219
72	SCIENCE GIVES BEFORE SHE IS ASKED	222
73	THE SCHOLAR IN OVERALLS	224
74	FURFURAL WANTS A JOB	227
75	COAL-OIL FROM COAL	230
76	A NEW PATH TO OBLIVION	233
77	MEDIUMS AND TRICKSTERS	237
78	TANGLING UP THE TIME LINE	240
79	ON TRANSLATING EINSTEIN	243
80	WHICH ORGAN WILL GIVE WAY FIRST	247
81	THE QUANTUM THEORY	248
82	HYDROGEN AT WORK	253
83	SCIENCE AND RELIGION AS ALLIES	256
84	SMASHING UP ATOMS	259
85	LAWS AND REVOLUTIONS IN SCIENCE	264
	INDEX	267

ILLUSTRATIONS

THE DARK HORSE NEBULA IN ORION . . . . . *Frontispiece*

FACING PAGE

AN INSIDE VIEW OF THE SINGING CRYSTAL 8

GROWING A BIG CRYSTAL OF ROCHELLE SALT 8

A CRYSTAL USED FOR TELEPHONING 8

HOW THE GIANT STARS WERE MEASURED 86

THE OAT PLANT, VISIBLE AND INVISIBLE 133

THE EINSTEIN CAMERA IN THE AUSTRALIAN DESERT . . . 204

HOW A LIGHT RAY IS DEFLECTED BY SUN 206

THE PHOTOGRAPHIC PLATE THAT CONFIRMED EINSTEIN . . 208

EXPERIMENTAL FURFURAL PLANT 228

FILLING STAND FOR COMPRESSING OXYGEN OR HYDROGEN . . 254

BANK OF 30 GENERATORS OF OXYGEN AND HYDROGEN . . . 254

FOG TRACKS OF RADIUM PROJECTILES 260

CHATS ON SCIENCE

CHATS ON SCIENCE

1

The Chattability of Science

Most people think of science as a serious and solemn thing, a strain upon the strongest intellect.

So it is for the pioneers of scientific progress, but not for those who merely follow along behind.

The layman does not exaggerate, in fact he does not begin to appreciate, the difficulty of original research, the devotion and self-sacrifice of men of science. A man may pursue a subject for years and then find that he has lost his labor through taking the wrong turn in the labyrinth of nature. He may count himself one of the fortunate if what he accomplishes in a lifetime is considered worthy of filling a footnote in some general compendium of science.

But however painful and slow a process may be the promotion of science, its results are intended to eliminate labor and economize time. The scientist toils that others may have an easier time. Road-making is hard, but joy-riding is not. It is owing to the labors of a long line of electricians from Faraday to Bell that the housewife is able to telephone the grocer to send over the ice-cream for dessert. If mechanicians **from** Hero of Alexandria to Otto of Cologne had not worked over engines, we would not be able to take a hundred-mile ride in an auto any fine day.

Science is a thought-saving device, and when applied to life it results in time-saving and labor-saving inventions.

Science means simplification. It substitutes a single rule for a million miscellaneous observations. To borrow a phrase from Poincaré, science consists in giving the same name to different things. The scientist links things together by whatever they have in common. If you have a lot of loose papers to carry, or sticks of kindling-wood, you will do it more easily if they are tied together in a single bundle. That is what the scientist is always doing, tying up fugitive facts into compact and portable packages. Learning the thirty-six combinations of the multiplication table is hard work, but once you have mastered this you become master of all the multiplications in the world. Newton's law, "Action and reaction are equal and opposite," covers in seven words all possible cases of the application of force.

Because some people have to study the sciences seriously, it is no reason why the rest of us should not chat about them or joke about them. We may make light of ponderous matters and even treat gravity with levity without danger of irreverence. If the reader finds a page dull he can skip over to another without fear of losing the thread of the story because there is none. I have purposely mixed up the pages lest the reader should be misled into thinking that he had got engaged in a continuous treatise and so would be compelled by his conscience to read longer than he liked. He can stop at the end of any ten minutes and—what is equally important—he can begin whenever he has ten minutes to spare. Only one favor I ask of him—that he do not put the book up on the shelves but keep it around where it is in his way and where he may pick it up any moment and so fill in the chinks of time. Possibly he may hit upon something that he did not know before and yet is worth knowing. Who can deny this possibility? Nobody till he has read the volume through. These are merely chats, yet not, I trust, mere chatter.

These chats as they have been written from week to week have been syndicated by Science Service to a chain of newspapers, and so some three million people have already had the opportunity of reading them. How many improved the opportunity I have no means of knowing. But I know that some did, for some have asked me if they could not get them in permanent form. Well, here is their chance, if they were in earnest about it.

2

The New World

The world we live in is a new world. Nobody ever lived in such a world before.

It is a bigger world because there are more people in it.

It is a smaller world because one can get around it quicker.

It is a more complex world because of the many new forces that have entered into it.

It is a simpler world to understand, for it has been more thoroughly studied and classified.

It is for the first time a known world, at least a knowable world. Practically all parts of it have now been explored. Most parts of it have been accurately mapped. Now that Amundsen has visited the south pole and Peary has visited the north pole, no place on the globe's surface can be regarded as inaccessible.

We can now for the first time take stock of our resources and calculate our potentialities. We know just how much land we have at our disposal. We know that we will never have any more land. We know pretty well what this land will grow and what it will not grow. We know how much food and what kinds each individual needs. We can then figure out how many people the earth can support at any given standard of life.

We cannot see underground, but from looking at the edges of the strata where it is tipped up and from boring into it a mile or more in various places we can tell about how much coal and oil, iron and copper, potash and phosphate we have to go on and we know that we can never get any more when this runs out.

In this new world of ours there is no more free land. The open range has gone forever. It is all staked out in private claims. Some flag floats over every bit of dry land. The last bit of No-Man's-Land left in the world, Spitzbergen, was appropriated during the late war. This means that if any nation is to get more land it must get it from some other nation.

There are many more nations than there were in the nineteenth century. Some twenty or more infant independencies are struggling for existence. If we call the cradle-roll of the new-born nationalities we find them scattered from the Balkans to the Baltic, from Ireland to Azerbaijan, from Palestine to Vladivostok; all new and untried factors in the world's affairs.

War is new. It is fought with weapons hitherto unknown.

Commerce is new. Strange commodities are carried by novel channels of trade.

Finance is new. The old standard is lost, and no one knows which nations are bankrupt and which solvent.

Science is new. It is outgrowing its clothes, its old formulas and theories.

Consequently it is more difficult than ever to predict the future or to apply the lessons of the past.

The historian Seeley once remarked, "When I hear a man say, 'History teaches us,' I say to myself that man is going to tell a lie, and he always does."

History cannot help us much now because it is the history of another and very different world from ours. So many unknown quantities have been introduced into our present problem that it cannot be solved by the old rules.

3

The Singing Crystal

As the lecturer walked down the aisle the crystal was dangling from his hand by a pair of insulated wires as though it were a portable lamp bulb. But instead of light the crystal was sending out sound. It was an orchestra in itself, playing Sousa's march, loud enough so that it could be heard all over the hall. It could sing like Galli-Curci, too, exactly like her, since it was her very voice we listened to later.

The crystal was about two inches tall and thick; looking like a tightly rolled collar with a piece of stout paper twisted around it. At the top and bottom were metal plates clamped together by screws so as to put the crystal under pressure. One wire was fastened to these end-pieces. The other was tied around the middle of the crystal. These wires ran to the other end of the room where they were fastened to a similar crystal in the same way. This crystal had a needle attached that followed the furrow of a phonograph record. This crystal served as the transmitter, and the other one as the receiver of the sound. A vacuum-tube amplifier magnified the music so that the whole audience could hear.

The first crystal took up the vibrations of the phonograph and converted them into electric waves that flowed out along the wire. The crystal at the other end took up the electric waves and converted them into sound-waves. One crystal sang to the other.

I took the singing crystal in my hand. It was

GROWING A BIG CRYSTAL OF ROCHELLE SALT
FOR EXPERIMENTAL PURPOSES

A CRYSTAL USED FOR TELEPHONING

A current is produced when such a crystal is put under pressure by screwing down the clamps. One wire pole of the circuit is attached to the ends and the other is wrapped around the middle.

Photographs by the Western Electric Co.

AN INSIDE VIEW OF THE SINGING CRYSTAL

This photograph was taken from one of the ends of a crystal of Rochelle salt and shows the striated sides converging toward a common center. The polar pieces for the electrical circuit are attached to the corners.

throbbing like a canary-bird's throat. When it was set upon the table it writhed and wriggled and marched across the board. If the music had been jazz I fear it would have shimmied.

A phonograph is unnecessary as a source of sound. Rub your finger ever so gently on one crystal, and its distant partner growls. Pinch one crystal and the other shrieks as though in pain. If you write on the piece of paper on which the crystal is laid, the scratching of your pen sounds like the rattling of a typewriter. Lay a watch on the crystal, and it sounds like a flivver badly out of repair.

Two such crystals make a complete telephone. You talk at one, and your friend holds his to his ear. When he speaks to his crystal you listen to yours. That is all there is to it. No battery, you see. The crystal provides its own electricity, making it from the force of your voice. One little crystal is enough to run two hundred telephones.

The lecturer provided each of us with a telephone receiver, all connected to a crystal by long wires. He then took the crystal with him out of doors, and from there he talked and sang to us. His voice sounded just as clear as if he had been in the room and just as cheerful as if it had not been raining hard on his bare head and Tuxedo.

The lecturer—I should have introduced him before, Mr. A. McLean Nicolson of the Research Laboratory of the Western Electric Company—started to work on this effect during the war. Presumably these sensitive crystals were found very useful in picking up German conversation or reporting German movements in No-Man's-Land between the lines. He has been able to grow crystals of any desired size up to two pounds weight and by drying out superficially their water of crystallization has been able to keep them in working order for several years. They improve by age and practice.

The best material for the crystal is Rochelle salt, a tartrate of sodium and potassium; what you drink when you take a Seidlitz powder and what you eat in the biscuit when you use tartrate baking-powder. The crystals that form at the bottom of a saturated solution of this salt are of two sorts, the same shape but differently set, like the left- and right-hand gloves, or a page of print and the printed page, or any object and its mirror image.

Such lopsided crystals—if you prefer Greek to English you may call them asymmetric—have a peculiar effect on a ray of light passing through them. The direction of vibration of the light-waves is twisted around toward the right by one kind of crystal, and toward the left by the other kind by the same amount. Now, the substances that affect light in this way show this peculiar electrical effect also. That is, if they are squeezed or twisted positive electricity collects at one part of the crystal and negative electricity at another, and if you connect these two points you get a current. This peculiarity was discovered in 1880 by Professor Pierre Curie of Paris, the same who later in conjunction with his wife discovered radium. The effect is called piezo-electricity in Greek, or pressure electricity in English. Quartz and tourmaline are piezo-electric.

So are camphor and sugar. I wondered how "The Rosary" would sound as sung by a lump of sugar, but I did not dare ask so frivolous a question before so serious an assemblage as the Washington Academy of Sciences.

Since compressing or twisting a crystal of this sort will give a current of electricity, so, conversely, applying a current of electricity to the crystal at the proper points will cause it to swell and twist. If the current fluctuates, the crystal will vibrate. That is how we get the singing crystal.

Several applications of piezo-electricity have been made, and others are possible. It was used during the war to measure the pressure inside cannon. The enormous pressure produced by modern powder reaches its highest point for only a fifty-thousandth of a second, and no ordinary pressure-gauge would be quick enough to register it or could stand such heat and force. But a crystal of tourmaline inserted in the bore will report the pressure by wire instantaneously to the electric meter outside. The temperature and pressure of the combustion of gasolene in an automobile engine can be determined in the same way.

Since a piezo crystal under certain pressures produces a definite electric current, such a crystal can be used as a standard, constant and convenient, for measuring any current by comparison.

Possibly the deaf may find here an aid, for it is conceivable that a tiny crystal hidden in the ear may replace the cumbrous trumpet, or battery and sound-receiver. Very likely more sensitive crystals may be produced that will extend the range of telephony. The war has given a new impetus to a line of investigation that has lain dormant for forty years.

4

The Lioness and the Hare

Once upon a time, many years ago, a hare boasted of her large family to a lioness. The lioness admitted her quantitative deficiency, but added that her one offspring was a lion. It was a conclusive retort—at the time. The lioness had no need to be disquieted by the success of her rival in maternity; indeed, she could rejoice in it, for there was no danger that the hares, however numerous, would crowd out the lions; on the contrary, if there were more hares, there would be more lions and better fed.

Now, however, conditions have so changed that the reply of the lioness is no longer satisfactory. We have put a stop to killing as a factor in the struggle for existence. The lion has his claws trimmed and his jaws muzzled by law. The battle is not to the strong, but the race is to the swift—breeder. The lion and the hare are compelled to live peaceably together and are placed on an equality. Questions are decided by counting noses, not by matching muscles or weighing brains. There is no reason to think that the propaganda of neo-Malthusianism will ever influence the hares, nor that any legislative bonus will increase the size of leonine families. Consequently lions are becoming extinct, and hares are multiplying all over the earth.

In its modern form, therefore, this fable teaches that the hares are bound to beat the lions in the long run, no matter how much bigger the latter may be or how much louder they can roar.

And having extracted this lesson of eugenics from the fable, I drop it right here. A fable is a single-barreled weapon, and if you attempt to get more than one shot out of it it is likely to explode, to the injury of the user. So I am not going to discuss the question whether the savage and predatory lion is a nobler beast than the meek and vegetarian hare and better fitted to populate the world. Still less am I going to identify with the lion and the hare any particular classes or races.

5

The Super-Rats

There is in the world a race of rats that love light rather than darkness, that prefer playing to eating, that seek the society of humans instead of shunning it, that appreciate music, and that do not bite. Big, clean, handsome white rats, that look you fearlessly in the face with their pretty pink eyes and pat you kindly with their pretty pink paws.

I know that such rat aristocrats exist because I 've seen them. And handled them. Not at first, I admit, for I am naturally shy in the presence of strange rats. But when I saw them come trooping out of the opened door of their habitation and pile up in the arms of their lady attendant, and the topmost one, standing on tiptoes and tail, reach up and kiss her nose, resisting his native ratty instinct to bite it—then I knew that the rat had been really reformed.

How was this wonderful transformation of native character accomplished? By eugenics and euthenics, or, if you prefer, by good breeding and good bringing up. No use starting the old discussion as to which is the more important, heredity or environment, nature or nurture, for if either is bad the other is no good. As for the former factor, these gentry have been bred for many generations from gentle rats. There was a strain of bad blood in the family. They had their Jukes, their congenital criminal class. Some were as wicked as a rat could be. Maternal infanticide and cannibalism must be about the lowest limit of criminality—at least for rats. But these black sheep in white fur have been segregated, and by careful and continuous selection of the better stock the new race has been evolved.

The Super-Rat has increased in some cases as much as three hundred per cent above standard. He carries a bit more fat than his ancestors and takes life rather more leisurely. He would probably if he were human make golf his exercise rather than tennis. But being deprived of the opportunity of either, he takes to the wheel, on which he does from one thousand to five thousand revolutions a day which amounts to from one to five miles—the equivalent for a man of a run from thirty to one hundred and fifty miles.

His brain has more than kept up with the growth of

the body. The brain of the Super-Rat is five per cent heavier in proportion to his total weight than with the ordinary rat. Presumably these new rats have more sense than their ancestors, but I neglected to ask if they had been put through the intelligence tests now employed on army recruits and college freshmen—those where you are set to putting round pegs into square holes and applying the rule of three to adjectives. I have heard that there are professors who spend more time educating their rats than their students.

But I did learn of a test of their musical suscepti- bilities. A phonograph was brought into the rat house, and it was found that they would stop eating to listen to the music. Elgar's "Capricieuse" played by Heifetz put them to sleep. The reader may draw his own in- ference as to their musical taste. I imagine that if I had read to them Browning's "Pied Piper of Hamelin" the rats would have been moved to tears by that epic tragedy of their race. There was a little shrine on the wall of one of the rooms with two tiny candles and a penny before it, but I could not discern the image of the deity—possibly it was the Rat Goddess of the Japanese. But whether the moral regeneration of the rats is in any measure due to the development of their religious nature I did not find out. I am inclined to think, however, that it is ascribed rather to plenty of vitamins and petting.

H. G. Wells once told of a "boom food" that made rats as large as lions. But they were as fierce as lions, too. It is not desirable that rats—or any other crea- tures—should grow bigger unless they grow better. Properly balanced food seems to do both. The reason why the Wistar Institute has gone into the rat raising business on such a large scale is because the rat comes nearest of any animal to being a miniature man. He has been the housemate of the human race from the time of the cave-dwellers.

I saw one group of rats that were having a hard time of it. The poor things looked so thin and miserable compared with the others! Oh, don't imagine that they were being badly treated. Quite the contrary; they had been especially favored. The label on their cage showed that they had been given, in addition to the ordinary diet, one of those foods that are advertised in our best magazines as especially nutritious. Probably I had better not mention the name of it. But it was evident to any eye that rats—and presumably human beings—were better nourished without it. It would be an immense saving in money and human life if such dietetic experiments were first carried out on rats. For instance, thousands of sufferers from pellagra or rickets might have been saved if we had known as much about dietary deficiencies as we do now.

Thirty is the factor that converts the rat figures into human figures. The growth of the rat from birth to maturity is thirty times as rapid as that of man. Multiplying the rat's age by thirty gives you the age when the man will be in the same stage of development as the rat. A rat three years of age is equivalent to a man ninety years of age. And what is more important, they may maintain the full vigor of maturity, as shown by the fertility of the female, for a period corresponding to sixty years. There is no race suicide in the rat family. I was introduced to Emily Jane, whose offspring now number some ten thousand although she had her first litter of pups only eighteen months ago. This would be equivalent—but perhaps the rule of thirty does not apply here.

Why have these new rats lost their fondness for a hole? Because they have no reason to hide. Why do they not run away at sight of man? Because they are not afraid of him. Why do they not bite him when they get a chance? For the same reason. Fearing is ever the father of fighting. Why should they fight, since they are unafraid? For forty generations they have known neither enemy, pestilence, nor famine. That corresponds to thirteen centuries on our time scale.

Think what a world this might be if since the time of Mohammed's Hejira there had never been a war, no human being had felt fear, none had suffered from want, none had lacked wholesome food or comfortable habitation or medical attention. Possibly by this time we might have become a race of super-men. Not Nietzsche's super-man, the "great blond beast," tyrannical, ruthless. But a generation of gentle folk, all handsome and healthy and long-lived and good mannered and peaceable—like these Quaker rats of Philadelphia.

6

SCIENCE BEGINS IN WONDER—BUT SHOULD GROW OUT OF IT

When a baby sees a strange object—and to a baby all objects are strange—first, he opens his mouth and stares at it; next, he sticks out his finger and tries to touch it; third, he grabs it and tries to do something with it.

These are the three stages through which individuals and races pass in their attitude toward the unknown in nature: first, wonder; second, curiosity; third, utilization. Each new lesson in humanity's book of knowledge is punctuated first with ! to be followed by ? and later perhaps by $.

Some persons and peoples remain always in the earliest infantile attitude of empty awe and take pride in it. They do not even attempt to pass to the stage of idle curiosity, as does the normal child. From the open mouth to the open mind is often a long and toilsome progress in the history of the race. The ancient Athenians had passed from the "Oh!" stage to the "Why?" stage but never reached the "What for?" stage. That is why they were overwhelmed by the barbarians, who did not know so much but knew how to kill people quite as well.

In the earlier culture stages people are curious only about "curiosities." They are not interested in the ordinary. It is the "Wonders of Science" period in literature. The museums are jackdaw nests of pretty stones, queer shells, and outlandish trinkets. Crowds flock to the sideshow tents to see the two-headed calf and bearded lady. They may even go so far as to wonder why the calf is bicephalous and the lady pogoniastic, but they do not even raise the more important question why most calves have only one head and most ladies no beard. They listen with eagerness to the tales of travelers, like Herodotus and Mandeville, who have been, or profess to have been, in remote regions. They are curious of all customs except their own, which, being customary, require no explanation. "Why do they act so?" they say of forcigners, but never, "Why do we act so?" though that is a question that they might more easily answer. Man began his study of the world with the more distant things. He gazed long at the stars before it occurred to him to look at the ground on which he stood, and longer yet before he tried to turn his attention inward to find out what was going on inside of his own head. Astronomy was well grown before geology was born, and psychology has only recently been admitted to the family of the sciences.

Ignorance is commonly alluded to as "darkness," but it is not so easy as that would imply. The darkness of space offers no impediment to the penetration of light, but the human mind often opposes a specific resistance to the entrance of a new idea—especially if it is a big idea that requires some rearrangement of the mental furniture before room can be found for it.

There are those who love darkness rather than light, not because their deeds are evil but just because they like to sit around in the dark and tell ghost-stories to one another. They prefer mystery where they can imagine whatever they wish, and they fear that science will

> Conquer all mysteries by rule and line,
> Empty the haunted air, and gnomed mine,
> Unweave a rainbow, as it erewhile made
> The tender-personed Lamia melt into a shade.

They even seem to regard God, quite blasphemously, as a great conjuror whose tricks may some time be exposed by some impertinent scientist who turns too much light upon the phenomena of nature. They do not know the simple geometrical principle that as the area of enlightenment enlarges it lengthens the circle of the surrounding darkness.

7

LET US LEAVE OFF LIVING ON LEAVINGS

Man occupies an unenviable position in the world. He is a parasite of parasites. He cannot draw his energy directly from the central source of the solar system, but must take it at second hand or third or fourth hand. He must get his food from the plants or from animals which in turn get it from the plants. Man is the latest comer upon this planet, a parvenu in mundane society. He lives on and off the lower forms of living beings, vegetable and animal, from which he derives sustenance and service. He is dependent upon them for his daily bread, and he must, for the most part, take what they give him and fix it up for his own purposes as best he can.

Man takes the milk from the suckling calf. He devours the embryo of the next generation of grain. He robs the sleeping silkworm of its homespun blanket. He steals the honey of the unborn bee. He takes from the musk-deer his last scent. He gets pearls from a diseased oyster. He gets perfume from a diseased whale. He gets ink from a diseased oak.

Man has picked up his plunder in a world-wide rummage sale. Anything that a plant or animal found useless and so packed away to get rid of, man has hunted out and made use of it. If a certain plant in its vital processes happens to produce a poisonous alkaloid, man seeks it and extracts it for medical purposes.

In ancient days the mightiest monarch knelt at the foot of a Mediterranean mollusk and said:

"Mr. Murex, I want a purple robe to display my dignity. Won't you give me a bit of dye to color it with?"

The mollusk looked up at the king with kindly condescension and replied:

"I believe I have a bit of stuff from which a purple dye might be manufactured, but it was of no use to me and smelled so bad that I stuck it away in a back corner of my shell. You are quite welcome to it if you can make any use of it."

So the king carefully extracted the drop of foul liquid, and after he had begged of a million of other mollusks he got enough to dye his purple robe.

In our time the chemist has freed men from the necessity of asking the snail for a hand-out, for he can manufacture royal purple by the ton. The dyes once confined to kings and potentates are now sold for ten cents a package in the corner drug-store. By this act the chemist has raised the common people to the ranks of royalty. The poorest person in the land is now "born to the purple." The test-tube is mightier than the sword.

But although we have secured a partial freedom from dependence in such particulars as this, our position is essentially unaltered. We still live for the most part on the chance bounty of nature and must hunt for what we might make to suit ourselves. We rely upon the green leaf to supply us with energy, although we have more brains and an equal access to sunshine.

When a man wants a new coat he must go to his flock and beg for it prettily: "Baa, Baa, Black Sheep, have you any wool?" and be quite content if he gets his three bags full. But to get it he must nurse the silly sheep from infancy as a mother cares for her child; he must feed and tend it, see that it is warm enough o' nights and safely sheltered; he must wash it and free it from vermin. And the wool when he gets it is not quite what he wants. It is short, shrinky stuff.

Whenever we want a pair of shoes we must go out and kill a calf. One does not have to be a sentimentalist or a vegetarian to feel that this is a painful necessity. There are few things more unsatisfactory and indispensable than leather. It is expensive, and it is growing scarcer, as pastures shrink and herds are reduced. It is the best material for bookbindings and furniture coverings, yet in a few years it is rolling off in yellow dust or cracking to pieces. A suit-case costs a fortune and weighs a ton, and yet at the end of vacation it looks too shabby for the garret. Gloves are clumsy and fragile.

One would think that man would be ashamed to be wearing hand-me-downs after he has lived several hundred thousand years on this earth. But he must be governed by practical considerations. He can't afford to be sentimental or squeamish. He must put his pride in his pocket as he did long before he had a pocket.

For beggars cannot be choosers. So long as man lives upon the hand-outs which he gets by going about from back door to back door, he can never call himself free and independent. Nor can he acquire a sufficient quantity of the rarer compounds in the world so that these commodities can be distributed freely among the common people.

8

ANCESTRAL SCANDALS OF SCIENCE

Tracing back the history of a science is like searching out a genealogy; one is sure to unearth something scandalous if he goes back far enough. John G. Saxe warned the would-be ancestor-worshiper of this danger in the familiar lines:

> Depend upon it, my snobbish friend,
> Your family thread you can't ascend,
> Without good reason to apprehend
> You may find it waxed at the farther end
>   By some plebeian vocation!
> Or, worse than that, your boasted line
> May end in a loop of a stronger twine,
>   That plagued some worthy relation!

The chemist handles with reverent awe the latest unearthed and earliest written text of his science, a scrap of Egyptian papyrus; but when he gets it translated he finds it is a counterfeiter's formula, a method of making base metals look like gold. Or else it is a recipe for cosmetics, which is also a form of counterfeiting.

The astronomer finds in a Babylonian brick the first record of the stars but discovers to his disgust that the cuneiform inscription is an astrological treatise, a fortune-teller hand-book.

Hero of Alexandria described the turbine steam-engine, the coin-in-a-slot machine, and other valuable inventions. But what were they invented for? So that the priests of the temple of Isis could perform fake miracles.

Pythagoras discovered the law of the hypotenuse—and was so happy over it that he killed a hundred oxen. It is hard for us to see why. But mathematics was to him a form of magic, otherwise he would not have been interested in it.

Paracelsus did much to advance medicine. We cannot yet dispense with the three drugs he introduced: mercury, opium, and antimony. But Paracelsus's real name was Bombast—and he lived up to it.

It is humiliating to confess, but the progress of science in its early days owed much to the false pretensions of its practitioners. Kings would not have kept a corps of men studying the stars unless practical returns had been proffered in the way of auguries. Chemists were subsidized for centuries because they promised the philosopher's stone and the elixir of life, promises not yet fulfilled.

Columbus would not have ventured to cross the Atlantic if he had not been wrong in his figuring about the size of the earth, and his royal backers would not have put up the money for the voyage if he had not told them wrongly that he could reach India that way.

Ponce de Leon was led to Florida by his search for a

mythical Fountain of Youth. Coronado explored the Kansas plains to find the fabulous Seven Cities of Cibola. The vain search for the impracticable north-west passage to Asia was the stimulus to exploration for a century.

Fortunately for the world, fictitious aims may lead to real results. The scientist has learned how to achieve greater miracles than he ever pretended to perform. Truth has grown up under the shadow of error, as infant oaks get their start under the shelter of worth-less weeds. In chasing a will-o'-the-wisp one may catch sight of a fixed star. Falsity has often served as a guide to truth.

If the alchemist and the astronomer had been frank with their royal patrons and said, "No, we cannot promise you gold from lead, or everlasting life, or the power of reading fate in the stars, but if you will grubstake us and our successors for two thousand years we may be able then to tell you the size of the universe and the structure of the atom," they would have been laughed at instead of getting a share of the king's bounty. Even had they added the further promise, "If given a chance to devote our lives to science we will, besides said increase of human knowledge, throw in dynamos, bridges, coal-tar dyes and the like," still the ancient monarchs, being near-sighted, like all men, would have refused to come down with the cash for the benefit of a remote posterity.

But science nowadays can show such practical profits that it is beginning to get funds for research without pretending to do more than it knows it can. Science can safely promise rich rewards for money spent in its advancement, but it cannot say when or in what coin the world will get dividends on such investment in futures.

9

Nature's Advertising

In these days when people are trying to draw a dividing line between essential and non-essential expenditure, some are inclined to call advertising wasteful and unwarranted. To them we would commend the biblical injunction, "Consider the lilies."

Why is a flower arrayed in a splendor exceeding that of Solomon? Because it is advertising its Spring Opening. "Free nectar on draft to-day," it announces to every bee and butterfly and humming-bird who passes by; and like the wily advertiser that it is, says nothing about the pollen it wants shifted from stamen to pistil by the aid of those who enter its attractive portals.

So it is with much, we do not know just how much, of the beauty that delights us in the vegetable and animal worlds. It is not that futile form of art which our decadent and dilettante esthetes praise, not "art for art's sake." It is applied art, purposive, businesslike. It accomplishes its object and then disappears. The wings of the butterfly, the varied hues and perfumes of the flowers, the plumage and the song of birds, such are but examples of nature's art in advertising. To him who in the love of nature holds communion with her visible forms a forest is as interesting and full of meaning as the bill-boards on Broadway.

You may say that the advertising poster and page are not always beautiful or tasteful. But neither always is nature's advertising—to our taste. The caw of the crow and the braying of the ass are not musical, but they are effective. The parrot displays combinations of color that would startle a Bakst. No woman is so devoid of taste as to dress as certain orchids do. But the parrot and the orchid succeed in making themselves conspicuous even amid the fierce competition of the tropical forest.

Nature does not always keep to the highest ethics in advertising. Much of it is deceptive. There are cheating animals, swindler insects, and confidence plants. The pitcher-plant displays a gorgeously colored signboard and takes in suckers by the offer of free drinks. The fly-traps and sundews entice their victims into their toils and then devour them. Some plants attract carrion flies by imitating the color and odor of decaying meat. Insects disguise themselves as flowers, leaves, or sticks in order to deceive their prey or their pursuers. Gay or grotesque beetles or butterflies may be merely pretending to be distasteful or ferocious while really ordinary and harmless.

Dame Nature spares no expense in the advertising department. Here she displays her most gaudy colors, her most striking designs, and her most attractive perfumes. The firefly runs a flash-light sign during the summer nights. Nature will scrimp elsewhere in order to be lavish where publicity is necessary.

The bird in the nest wears dowdy clothes in order that her mate who goes out in society may be dressed as well as any of his associates. In the design of a tree the structural strains are figured closely to secure tne greatest possible economy of material consistent with the strength necessary for its height, its burden, and the wind pressure; but when it comes to flowering, nature is no longer niggardly. The wasted petals strew the ground like the discarded dodgers on the sidewalk, and if one seed in ten thousand finds a lodgment, the expenditure is worth while.

The argus-eyed tail of the peacock, the trailing plumage of the bird of paradise, and the long, sweeping feathers of the lyre-bird, are hampering to movement and expensive to keep up. They are examples of what Professor Veblen calls ''competitive expenditure.'' But it pays to advertise, and often to advertise lavishly and with seeming recklessness. The fossil beds are filled with the remains of species which went into bankruptcy because they failed to advertise or advertised unwisely.

A study of paleontology, that is, of the stone records of success and failure in the vegetable and animal kingdoms, from the beginning of time would be a profitable occupation for any business man.

10

A Crazy Experiment and What Came of It

I suppose every scientific man occasionally tries experiments that he would not care to confess to his colleagues. Crazy ideas will pop up in the best regulated brains from some subconscious cellar, and sometimes they are tried out, on Saturday afternoon when there is nobody else around, just to see what will come of them. They do not appear in the published reports, unless they happen to succeed, in which case the audacious experimenter will claim credit for foresight in undertaking an operation that ordinary minds would have condemned in advance as absurd.

Now, it is interesting to observe that such erratic and irrational experimentation is distinctly recommended by the philosopher who laid down the laws of experimental science that have in the three centuries since accomplished such amazing achievements.

Lord Bacon, after listing in his precise and orderly manner all the various ways that we may be guided in our researches by theory, observation, and previous experiment, concludes quite unexpectedly by adding a new category, what he calls the experiments of a madman and defines as follows:

When you have a mind to try something not because reason or some other experiment leads you to it but simply because such a thing has never been attempted before.

The leaving, I say, of no stone in nature unturned, for the magnalia of nature generally lie out of the common roads and beaten paths so that the very absurdity of the thing may sometimes prove of service. But if reason go along with it, that is, if it be evident that an experiment of this nature has never been tried, then it is one of the best ways and plainly shakes the folds out of nature.

The example Bacon gives of such unprecedented experiments is of peculiar interest to us:

But of what I may call close distillation no man has yet made trial. Yet it seems probable that the force of heat, if it can perform its exploits of alteration within the enclosure of the body, where there is neither loss of the body nor yet means of escape, will succeed at last in handcuffing this Proteus of matter and driving it to many transformations; only the heat must be so regulated and varied that there be no fracture of the vessels.

No one should be disheartened or confounded if the experiments which he tries do not answer his expectation. For though a successful experiment be more agreeable, yet an unsuccessful one is often times no less instructive. And it must ever be kept in mind (as I am contiually urging) that experiments of Light are even more to be sought after than experiments of Fruit.

What Bacon was "continually urging," that "experiments of Light"—those that lead to enlightenment on fundamental principles—"are even more to be sought after than experiments of Fruit"—those that bring practical results—needs more than ever to be kept in mind at the present day, when public and employers are impatient of research that does not bring immediate and profitable returns.

So it is worthy of notice that the example that Bacon cites as the experiment of a madman, that is, destructive distillation, has been peculiarly productive of both Light and Fruit. Applied to coal it has given us coke for metallurgy, gas for cities, and coal-tar products of innumerable variety and inestimable value. Applied to petroleum in the cracking process it has increased the yield of gasolene by about two million gallons a day. By thus "handcuffing this Proteus of matter and driving it to many transformations" light has been thrown upon the structure of the molecule and the chemistry of life.

11

EINSTEIN IN WORDS OF ONE SYLLABLE

A friend of mine—I don't know him personally, but any man is a friend of mine who buys a book of mine—writes to me, "If you will put Einstein's theory of relativity in words of one syllable perhaps I can understand it."

Now that is a foolish notion—though he be a friend of mine. Short words may be easier to pronounce but are not easier to understand. Some of the most difficult words in the language to grasp or define are monosyllables; for instance, mass, force, law, love, God. Chinese is a monosyllabic language but not easy to learn. Einstein's idea is hard to get, not because he uses big words, but because it is a big idea. Einstein does better than put his theory in words of one syllable. He puts it in symbols of one letter. But even those who understand the algebraic language do not find it easy to follow him.

Besides, how can I be expected to explain Einstein's theory of relativity in words of one syllable when "Einstein" has two syllables, "theory" three, and "relativity" five?

But anything to oblige a friend. So here goes:

THE EINSTEIN PRIMER

If you were on a train and saw a train on the side track slip by your pane of glass, you could not tell which train moved if yours did not jolt. You might think that this train was at rest and that that one moved back, or that both moved but not at the same rate or the same way. The point would be which way you looked at it.

If now you were in a tight chest, as big as a room, that stood on the ground, you would feel the down pull which we call your weight. It is said to be due to a "force." But if the chest were off in space where there was no force from the earth to act on it and the chest were pulled up by a rope at the same rate as a mass falls, you would feel the floor press up on your feet just the same as when you stood on the ground. You know how it feels when you are in a lift that goes up with a jerk. If while you were in this chest off in space you should throw a ball up into the air it would go up a way, then fall down to the floor. So it looks to you; though to a man not in the chest it seems that the floor moved up and caught up with the slow ball. If you should fire a shot straight from the right side of the chest to the left, its path would seem curved down at the end as it would on the earth. So, then, a ray of light, which, too, we say moves straight, would seem to your curved when it passed through the chest, as though it, like the shot, had been pulled down by some force. But there is no down force in this case, for the chest is not near the earth. It is just due to the fact that the chest moves up with more and more speed in the same way as a mass falls to the earth.

Then we must think that a ray of light near a large mass would not move in a straight line but in a curve. It would act just as if there were a force to pull it in. This has been found to be so. As the light from a star goes past the sun its track is bent to the sun as though the sun pulled the ray in a curved path, as it does the earth. So when the sun is made dark by the moon the stars round about it seem pushed out of place. They do not stand so close as they do on the star map when the sun is not in their midst.

Then, too, the sphere that moves round the sun most near to it does not quite close up the ring of its path at the end of a year as it should by the old law. The new law shows why this is so.

A third test of the new law has now been passed. The light

and dark lines that are seen in a beam of light when it is bent
out of its course by a wedge of glass should be pushed to the
red end of the band if the light comes from large stars like
the sun. A long light wave like the red should show more
shift than the short waves of blue light. Such a shift has
been seen in the light from the sun.

Some strange things must be true if the new law holds good.
First, we must say that mass and weight are not fixed but
change when the thing moves, though the change is slight
save at high speeds. But near the speed of light the change
is great. A thing must weigh more when it moves fast. If
a rod goes at great speed in the line of its length it will
not seem so long as if it were at rest. No mass can be made
to move as swift as light.

A clock in a state of rest does not show the same time as
a clock that moves at high speed. As it moves fast it seems
to slow up through space. If a man could move through
space with the speed of light he would not grow old as seen
from a point of rest.

It is a matter of choice if we say that the earth goes round
the sun or that the sun goes round the earth. It all lies in
the point of view. If a ring is seen to be one foot through
when a rule is laid on it, it will be pi times that length
round the rim. But if there is a great weight put in the mid
point of the ring, then the line around the rim will not be
so long as if the space were free. It will be less than pi
times the line that cuts through the ring at its mid point.
If a thin steel disk whirls round fast its rim will seem to
shrink like a hot tire on the wheel of a cart.

It seems, then, that the scheme of points and lines that we
got from the Greeks, and that is still taught in our schools,
is not quite true when we come to deal with time and space
as a whole. Space would be naught if there were no time.
Time would be naught if there were no space. The two must
join to form a sort of fixed frame or mesh in which all things
are set. At each point, say the point where you stand, four
lines cross and lead out straight in the four ways. One line
runs up and down; the next runs right and left; the third

runs back and forth; and the fourth runs from time past to time to come. To fix a thing we must know its point on the time line as well as its points on the three space lines. To place an act we must know when as well as where it came to pass.

Mass in some way warps this mesh of space and time. A mass as it moves forms a sort of a crease or ridge. A mass that is at rest in space of course moves on the time line. A mass as it moves from point to point must take the track that is most long through the mesh of space and time.

Space as a whole may be closed up in the form of a sphere or roll and in that sense may be said to have no end, though it may not be so large as we used to think. A ray of light that starts out from the sun may not go on straight for all time but may go round the sphere of space and come back at the end of a long time to the place it set out from at the first.

All this is not, as you may think, just a new and queer way to look at the world. It can be put to proof in some points to see if it is the true view and has, as I have said, come out well on three such tests. It starts a new lead for man's thought.

12

Perfumes from Poison Gas

On my desk stands a tiny vial half full of a colorless oil. Although there is so little of it it is very valuable, for it costs two hundred dollars a pound.—— Oh, no, I did not pay that for it. It was given to me by a man whose delightful business it is to make the world sweeter. For although this liquid is so expensive, it is comparatively cheap. You may be paying much more for it than this whether you buy it at a fashionable perfumer's, a ten-cent store, or a florist's. For this is the concentrated essence of the odor of violets. If the violet will smell as sweet under any other name, you may call it by the chemical cognomen, methyl heptin carbonate. Of course the flower fragrance or the finished scent is not a single substance but a complex and variable mixture of divers ingredients of this sort. The chemist who is to compete with or surpass Nature in her fine arts must have the nose of an artist as well as the mind of a scientist.

The sample of the primary material that I have in hand differs from the flower whose name it bears in one respect. It emphatically lacks the modesty associated with the violet. It is insistent and persistent, aggressive and clamorous. It smells as though all the violets in the country had combined to lure an up-to-date publicity man to advertise their spring opening. One day I took it with me to New York to illustrate a talk. I stuck the stopper in tight, wrapped it in my handkerchief, and buried it in my vest pocket. Yet when I entered the lobby of the hotel a young man near by nudged his companion and said, ''Where 's the dame with the big bunch of violets?'' They looked in my direction, and I tried to evade detection by also sniffing and smiling and looking about. But I felt my face turning red—or violet.

If you inhale a full whiff from the open bottle, the odor deafens your nose as the blare of a bass horn deafens your ear, if too close. Dilute the liquid, and it smells more like violets than when pure. Keep on reducing it, and you reach a point where it matches the odor of the flower. This is characteristic of the chemicals in general. The effect depends upon the amount. Quantity may reverse quality. A small dose of strychnine stimulates the bodily machinery. A larger dose stops it altogether. On the other hand, many a man has been foiled in an attempt to commit suicide because he took an overdose of arsenic.

The allied senses of smell and taste are exceedingly skilful chemists. They stand forever at the gates to see that only pure food and air enter the bodily citadel. Cooks and perfumers must also be good chemists to pass their products through this inspection.

But the most interesting thing about this perfume of mine is its origin. It came from a factory instead of a flower. It is a triumph of man's ingenuity instead of being the chance bounty of nature. We may take a peculiar pride in it, for here the chemist has taken one of the most horrible products of modern science and not only rendered it harmless but actually transfigured it into something delightful. The Bible tells us to beat our swords into plowshares and our spears into pruning-hooks. The chemist, then, is applying the biblical injunction to modern warfare when he turns a poison gas into a perfume.

This violet essence is made from phosgene and castor-oil, a poison and a purgative. But do not imagine that either of these unpleasant substances is contained in the final product. This is as pure as is perfume that the violet plant manufactures out of the manure that is put into the soil.

The laws of heredity do not apply in chemistry. A chemical compound does not inherit the characteristics of its parents. This is the first lesson that a student in chemistry should learn; but it is sometimes the last that he does learn. I have had lots of fun with this vial of violet, using it as a test of the power of suggestion on the imagination. When I try it on a lady friend by removing the stopper for an instant and wafting a whiff of it in her direction, she is likely to exclaim: "Oh, what an exquisite violet! Where did you buy it?"

When I tell her what it is made from, her expression usually changes from delight to either disgust or pain as she says: "Yes, I smell the castor-oil now," or, "Oh, it burns my lungs. How our poor boys in France must have suffered!"

Now, salt contains chlorine, but perhaps I ought not to let the secret out lest when I pass the salt to a friend he should seize his napkin and make a gas-mask of it to escape the fumes. Gypsum contains sulphur, but yet nobody objects to the presence of a plaster bust in the room on the ground that it smells like the lower regions. Chemical reactions change completely the substances concerned. It makes no manner of difference where the materials come from. Castor-oil is used simply because it has a long carbon chain that is needed in this case. Phosgene, whose chemical name is carbonyl chloride is used because it can furnish the required carbonyl group; also because we had a lot of it left over at the end of the war that we had no further use for as poison gas and hoped we never would have. Some of it is used in the manufacture of dyes, such as auramine yellow, Victoria blue, and wool green. I wonder whether the sudden popularity of yellow sweaters and blue silk and green woolen wear is due to a demand of popular taste—or to the left-over lots of phosgene.

Another beneficent transformation of the infernal phosgene is using it as an aid in the cure of consumption. In this healing mission its aid is a chemical almost as corrosive to the bodily tissues, carbolic acid. But from carbolic acid is made guiacol, an oil contained in beechwood tar and used in tuberculosis. If this now is combined with phosgene, its healing virtue is enhanced. So out of two virulent poisons is made a medicine, and what was designed to destroy the lungs may be turned to curing them.

This is as pleasant a thought as the former, that the phosgene that was made to still the heart of an enemy may now be employed in its perfume form to quicken the heart of a lover. Would that all the left-overs of the war could be so happily transmuted! Will not our spiritual directors—or the psychologists who now aspire to their functions—follow the example of the chemists and discover a way to transmute the poison gas of hate into the healing and fragrance of love?

13

FRANKLIN'S FORESIGHT

Franklin's fame has been somewhat obscured by the fact that he is famous in so many different fields. Nobody can write a history of American literature, politics, education, journalism, economics, diplomacy, philanthropy, or philosophy without giving a chapter to Franklin. But the world distrusts a many-sided man and particularly a wit; therefore Franklin's solid contributions to natural and social science are apt to be underestimated.

Everybody knows the story of his experiment with the kite and the key, which proved that the tiny sparks that could be got from cat's fur in the dark were of the same sort as the thunderbolts that tore trees to splinters. But not everybody knows that we owe to Franklin's ingenuity the terms "positive" and "negative" electricity which have been in use ever since and are so firmly fixed in our minds that we can hardly conceive of any other way of thinking about electrical processes.

Franklin knew that there were two opposite kinds of electrification. A French physicist, Dufay, had discovered a few years before that a glass rod becomes electrified when you rub it with silk and that a stick of sealing-wax becomes electrified when you rub it with cat's fur. But the two bodies are electrified in different and contrary ways. A pith-ball that would be attracted by the glass rod would be repelled by the sealing-wax stick and vice versa. It seemed then as though there were two different kinds of electricity, and Dufay called the kind on the glass "vitreous electricity" and the kind on the sealing-wax "resinous electricity."

But Franklin was an economical man. He did not want to spend twopence where a penny would do. He did not want to use two ideas where one would do. Since these two electricities act just alike except in their opposition to each other, and since they neutralize each other when brought together, why not, thought

Franklin, assume that there is only one electricity and that a body merely gets a little more or less of it by rubbing? Franklin was a business man before he became a scientist, and so he carried his bookkeeping over into his new field and conceived of electrification as a sort of debit and credit system.

To show you what a close shot at long range Franklin was I will quote his definition of electricity:

The electrical matter consists of particles extremely subtle, since it can permeate common matter, even the densest, with such freedom and ease as not to receive any appreciable resistance.

But this was too simple a notion to suit succeeding scientists, and so for more than a hundred and fifty years they held the two-fluid theory and refused to believe that electricity consisted of particles. Now, however, the existence of the subtle particles has been proved. "Electrons" we call them. They can be tracked, caught, and counted although too small to be seen. The other and opposite kind of electricity consists of atoms of ordinary matter minus these electrons.

Right here Franklin's foresight failed him and his luck turned against him. He had no possible way of telling which kind of electrification was due to the excess of the electrical particles and which to the deficiency, which state should be called "positive" and which "negative." It was a matter of chance, and he made the wrong choice!

For we now know that the free flying particles of electricity, the electrons, are of the "negative" sort, while the matter from which they have been subtracted is "positively" electrified.

But it is too late to exchange the terms now, and so we shall have to continue this confusing use for all time, just as we continue to call the end of the magnetic needle that points north the north pole, although we know that it should be the south.

14

EARLY BIRDS

The youngest man to receive a Nobel award is Dr. Niels Bohr of Copenhagen, who in 1922 was awarded the prize for the greatest discovery in physics. He was only thirty-seven then, and he was only twenty-eight when he startled the world by his bold conception of the atom as a sort of solar system in which the sun is represented by a nucleus of positive electricity and the planets by particles of negative electricity revolving around it with amazing speed. On this theory he was able to calculate just what shiftings in the orbits of these planetary electrons would give off light of the particular wave-length to make each line of the spectrum.

But it was a man even younger who in the same eventful year, 1913, made a still greater contribution to our knowledge of the interior of the atom. Henry Moseley, the Englishman, was only twenty-six when he found a way to analyze the elements by the reflection of X-rays from their atoms. This led him to "the most important generalization in the history of chemistry since Mendeleef's Periodic Law," the idea that the chemical properties of an element depend upon the number of free charges of positive electricity upon its nucleus. This shows us that there are ninety-two possible elements from hydrogen, the lightest, to uranium, the heaviest, and they are now all known but four.

Two years later young Moseley was killed at Gallipoli, and the premature extinction of his brilliant brain was one of the greatest losses of the Great War, a loss that no territorial gain can compensate; and it was, as we now know, a useless sacrifice, for Gallipoli has gone back to the Turks. "Some one had blundered."

In the history of science we often observe that epoch-making ideas have sprung from the brains of young men. Svante Arrhenius, the Swede, was only twenty-four when he devised the electrolytic theory of solution, the idea that salts are decomposed in water to positive and negative parts. Kekulé, the German, was twenty-eight when he hit upon the theory of types, which led him at the age of thirty-six to the symbol of the benzene ring. Berthelot, the Frenchman, was only twenty-four when he began his career in what he called "creative chemistry" by the synthesis of benzene compounds. William Crookes, the Englishman, was twenty-nine when he discovered thallium by the spectroscope, a new metal by a new method. Emil Fischer, the German, was twenty-three when he discovered the hydrazine reaction that led to the analysis and synthesis of the sugars. Perkin, the Englishman, was eighteen when he discovered the first aniline dye, mauve. Pasteur, the Frenchman, was twenty when he became intrigued with the puzzle of the right- and left-handed crystals of tartaric acid, which six years later he solved by making the inactive racemic acid by combining the two forms.

Twenty years later the explanation of this phenomenon burst simultaneously into the brains of two young men, the Frenchman, Le Bel, and the Dutchman, van't Hoff. The former was twenty-seven, and the latter was twenty-two. Van't Hoff was still a student when he published his eleven-page pamphlet on "The Structure of the Atoms in Space," and how he did get laughed at by his elders for his crazy notion! Isaac Newton, after telling how he worked out the binomial theorem, the method of tangents, the differential and integral calculus, the theory of colors, and the law of gravitation, concludes:

All this was in the two plague years of 1665 and 1666, for in those days I was *in the prime of my age for invention*, and minded Mathematicks and Philosophy more than at any time since.

The words I have italicized are worth noting, since Newton was born in 1642.

Albert Einstein conceived the idea of his theory of relativity when he was eighteen and published it at twenty-six. He is, as we should expect, an advocate of shortening up the school period and making it more practical, so that the student can get at his life-work earlier. This at least seems the best plan for brilliant minds like these, and educators are coming to the conclusion that special facilities should be afforded such, so that they may advance as fast as they can without waiting for their slower schoolmates. To give one young man of this sort the peculiar training he needs will benefit the world more than the education of a whole collegeful of the ordinary caliber.

Oliver Wendell Holmes used to say of infant prodigies that those who get up so early in the morning are likely to be very conceited all the forenoon and very sleepy all the afternoon. But this doesn't seem to apply to the cases we have here considered.

15

A Dangerous Mental Malady

The progress of mankind has been in all ages greatly retarded and at times altogether prevented by a curious sort of disease of the mind technically known as neophobia. In a case of hydrophobia the mere sight of water is said to arouse disgust, fear, and even furious anger. In a case of neophobia the symptoms are similar but the cause is different. The neophobic patient shows marked aversion and resentment at the sight of anything new. The disease is very prevalent, and there are no drugs known that will cure it, except poisons. We all seem to carry about the germs of it, for any of us is liable to manifest mild symptoms, and in certain countries and certain centuries it has been epidemic.

I came across a striking case of neophobia the other day in a letter written in March, 1825, by Thomas Creevey, when a bill for the construction of the first railroad line was introduced into Parliament. This is what he felt about it:

I have come to the conclusion that our Ferguson is *insane*. He quite foamed at the mouth with rage in our Railway Committee in support of this infernal nuisance—the loco-motive Monster, carrying *eighty tons* of goods, and navigated by a tail of smoke and sulphur coming thro' every man's grounds between Manchester and Liverpool. . . . Well—this devil of a railway is strangled at last.—Today we had a clear majority in committee in our favour and the promotors of the Bill withdrew it and took their leave of us.

This reminds us of the speech of Sir Charles Napier in the House of Commons when it was proposed to introduce steam power into the navy:

Mr. Speaker, when we enter Her Majesty's naval service and face the chances of war, we go prepared to be hacked in pieces, to be riddled by bullets or to be blown to bits by shot and shell; but, Mr. Speaker, we do not go prepared to be boiled alive.

The same temper was manifested by the Roman sage, Seneca, when he denounced the waterworks and heating systems that were being introduced into Roman houses and the buildings of several stories that were beginning to appear on the Palatine Hill. "These towering tenements," he said, "are dangerous to the persons who dwell in them." Dangerous to their morals, he meant, of course; not that he was afraid of the building falling down. "Believe me," he adds, "that was a happy age before the days of architects, before the days of builders." "A thatched roof once covered free men; under marble and gold dwells slavery." If he had seen a modern thirty-story sky-scraper the Latin language would not have been sufficient to express his emotions.

When Coryate in the seventeenth century came back to England from his travels in Italy he brought back an outlandish implement known as a "forke," and aroused much ridicule for using it for holding meat instead of his fingers. It was regarded as an insult to Providence that a man should be ashamed to touch wholesome food with his fingers.

Can a man be a Christian if he wears trousers? This question came up for decision by the ecclesiastical authorities when the Bulgarians were converted. They did not want to give up their national costume; but none of the early Christians wore trousers, and it was doubtful whether they were consistent with the new religion. Nowadays when a missionary converts a savage race the first thing he insists upon is that the man wear trousers regardless of the climate.

In Shakspere's time the feminine rôles were played by boys. When in 1629 a French troupe played at Blackfriars with women taking the women's parts they were "hissed, hooted and pippin-pelted from the stage."

When spectacles were introduced under the auspices of the Royal Society they were condemned as "impostors" and demoralizing, for "they would give one man an unfair advantage over his fellow, and every man an unfair advantage over every woman, who could not be expected, on esthetic and intellectual grounds, to adopt the practice." The Rev. Mr. Crosse, vicar of Chew Magna, Somersetshire, regarded "the use of the newly invented optick glasses as immoral, since they perverted the natural sight and made all things appear in an unnatural and therefore false light."

We can all remember the opposition to automobiles on the start, but it is hard to realize that once carts were so unpopular that when the Emperor Aurelian made his triumphal entry into Antioch he did not dare to use one.

The first coal shipped to Philadelphia in 1803 was not burned but used as gravel to make sidewalks. When Colonel George Shoemaker tried to sell a few wagonloads of coal in the same city he was driven from the streets and threatened with arrest.

When bath-tubs were first installed in the United States in the forties the papers attacked them as extravagant and undemocratic, and the doctors denounced them as dangerous to health. As usual, government was called upon to restrict or suppress the novelty by special taxes and licenses. In 1843 Virginia put a tax of thirty dollars a year on bath-tubs, and in 1845 a Boston municipal ordinance made such bathing unlawful except on medical advice.

The first printed books had to be sold as manuscripts because of the prejudice against printing. The learned men of Italy sneered at the invention as a barbarous German innovation.

The first ship-load of saltpeter sent to England from Chile could not find a buyer and had to be thrown into the sea.

The first bananas shipped to London could not be sold at any price or even given away in the slums but were left to rot because nobody would eat them.

When they were first introduced into England potatoes were denounced as injurious to society and tomatoes as injurious to morality.

All this is history now and so merely amusing. But it may make us stop a minute to consider if we are to-day opposing some similar innovation from unconscious neophobia.

16

THE SILKWORM'S RIVAL

Man has entered into active competition with the silkworm, and although the worm has the advantage of several million generations of previous practice in the art of silk making, man is rapidly catching up. The output of artificial silk has increased fivefold during the last twenty years, while the output of natural silk has only gained fifty per cent. Nearly half of what seems silk to the eye comes nowadays from the factory instead of the cocoon. About forty million foreign feet are now incased in synthetic silk stockings made in America. Over two billion yards of synthetic thread are spun out in a day in the factories of the United States, and if each thread consists of twenty filaments the total length of filaments produced in five days would more than suffice to reach the sun.

Artificial silk is not silk and should never be sold as such. But if it is, it is not so much because the salesman desires to deceive as it is because the public is unwilling to credit the chemist with the creation of something new or to believe that he can make anything so good as is made by a worm. Of late this unnatural prejudice in favor of nature is being overcome, and the new synthetic fibers are being marketed by their manufacturers, as they should be, under synthetic names. Some of the trade-names are viscose, lustron, fibersilk, luster-fiber, baronette, Givet silk, soie de Paris, Glanzstoff, artiseta, lustracellose. There are a lot of others that I omit to mention because I can't remember them.

There are four different modes of manufacture, but the raw material is essentially the same, cellulose. This is the substance of wood, paper, and cotton, so that it is cheap and abundant enough; but the difficulty is to dissolve it so that it can be squirted out of the tiny holes in the spinneret to form the fibers. Water will not dissolve paper pulp, of course, nor will any ordinary solvent except strong acids and alkalis.

The first person to solve the problem was a Frenchman, Count de Chardonnet, who in 1884 deposited with the French Academy of Sciences a sealed document. Three years later this was opened and found to contain a method of making artificial fiber by treating cellulose with nitric acid. The resulting compound, which is a mild form of guncotton, can be dissolved in alcohol and ether, like the common collodion that we use to cover our skinned knuckles. But the nitric had to be thoroughly eliminated from the yarn; otherwise it was too inflammable.

Another process, invented by the French and worked by the Germans, got the cellulose into fluid form by dissolving it in a solution of copper and ammonium salts.

In the making of viscose a third method is employed. Wood pulp, such as is used in paper making, is treated with strong soda lye and then with carbon disulphide. This brings the cellulose into solution as an orange liquid. This is forced through minute holes in a platinum nozzle into dilute acid, which hardens each fine stream into solid fiber, and the sulphide is then removed.

During the war another form of soluble cellulose found extensive employment as "scac," or dope for airplane wings. This is the acetate, made by dissolving cotton or wood-pulp in the concentrated acid of vinegar, acetic. Lustron is made by this process.

These various kinds of artificial fibers differ from one another, and all of them differ from natural silk. And in this difference lies their value. For fabrics can be woven out of natural and artificial silk with cotton or wool in any desired combination. The fabric at first may look white and uniform, but if it is dipped in baths of various dyes each thread will attach a particular tint, and a complicated design will be brought out in color.

The artificial fibers and the coal-tar dyes make a brilliant combination, and through the aid of this alliance our world has become more colorful and cheerful. Sweaters and shawls, hats and hose, neckties and underwear, have blossomed out in varied hue like the flowers that bloom in the spring. The knitting-machine has taken a new spurt and is now running a race with the loom. Our ladies may now wear synthetic lace that is shadowed by no thought of toilsome fingers and bent shoulders. They may wear synthetic furs without the sacrifice of wild life.

Man is no longer dependent upon what he can pick up in the plant or animal kingdoms, for the new fiber can be made in any form desired, flat or round, smooth or rough, thick or thin, and of any length. A single filament may be run out thousands of yards without knot or break.

The man-made fiber is not so strong as the worm-made silk, especially when wet; but what interfered with its popularity at first was the fact that it was lacking in "scroop." The scroop, as the sound of the word suggests, is the audible evidence of the presence of silk. What was the use of owning a silk petticoat if nobody can hear it as you pass by? So thought the ladies of former days, but the fashion changed, and now the preference is for silent silk.

17

How Scientific Inspiration Comes

Science is built up by patient and persistent labor, most of it drudgery of the hardest kind. But it is not altogether done by work of the bricklayer sort, the slow fitting together of fact upon fact and cementing them in place with the mortar of logic. There must come to somebody some time a vision of the edifice as a whole, the fundamental theory of the thing complete and perfect. This vision may come in a flash quite like the inspiration of the author or artist, and often when the mind is not consciously working on the problem but is, so to speak, off guard. It seems almost as though the answer were being whispered to him from without by some one who had watched with sympathy his fruitless efforts to solve it.

We find in the biographies of men of science frequent references to this so curious sensation of inspiration. One of the most explicit is the account given by the German chemist, Kekulé, of how he came to hit upon the ring formula for the benzene molecule. The twenty-fifth anniversary of this discovery was celebrated in

1890, and on that occasion Kekulé told how he came to conceive the idea of atomic linkages which has served as a guide to research ever since. It was during his *Wanderjahr* when he was living in London, at the age of twenty-two. He was in the habit of discussing chemistry with a friend living on the opposite side of the city, and this often kept him up late. He says:

One fine summer evening I was returning by the last omnibus, outside as usual, through the deserted streets of the metropolis which are at other times so full of life. I fell into a reverie (*Träumerei*), and, lo, the atoms were dancing before my eyes! Whenever, hitherto, these diminutive creatures had appeared to me, they had always been in motion, but up to that time I had never been able to discern the nature of their motion. Now, however, I saw how, frequently, two smaller atoms united to form a pair; how a larger one embraced two smaller ones; how still larger ones kept hold of three or even four of the smaller; whilst the whole kept whirling in a giddy dance. I saw how the larger ones formed a chain, dragging the smaller ones after them but only at the ends of the chain. I saw what our Past Master, Kopp, my highly honored teacher and friend, has depicted with such charm in his "Molecular-Welt"; but I saw it long before him. The cry of the conductor, "Clapham Road," awakened me from my dreaming, but I spent a part of the night in putting on paper at least sketches of these dream forms. This was the origin of the structure theory.

This gave him the conception of the chain formula for the ordinary hydrocarbons of the paraffin series, but benzene known to have the composition of C_6H_6 could not be so pictured, and this whole field of the aromatic hydrocarbons was an impenetrable mystery. Here again the imps of his subconscious, or what Socrates called his demon, came to his aid when he was professor at Ghent:

I was sitting, writing at my text-book, but the work did not progress. My thoughts were elsewhere. I turned my chair to the fire and dozed. Again the atoms were gamboling before my eyes. This time the smaller groups kept modestly in the background. My mental eye, rendered more acute by repeated visions of this kind, could now distinguish larger structures of manifold conformation, long rows, sometimes closely fitted together, all twining and twisting in snake-like motion. But, look! What was that? One of the snakes had seized hold of its own tail and the form whirled mockingly before my eyes. As if by a flash of lightning I awoke, and this time also I spent the rest of the night in working out the consequences of the hypothesis.

And Kekulé concludes with this bit of advice and warning:

Let us learn to dream, gentlemen, then perhaps we shall find the truth. . . . But let us beware of publishing our dreams before they have been put to the proof by the waking understanding.

Kekulé was certainly excusable in indulging a bit in day-dreaming, for he did not have much time to sleep. No eight-hour day for him, and he never charged for overtime. He says in this autobiographical talk:

During many years I managed to do with four and even three hours' sleep. A single night spent over my books did not count. It was only when two or three came in succession that I thought I had done anything meritorious.

In pursuing this hard course of life he was following the advice of his great teacher, Liebig, who said to him:

If you want to be a chemist, you will have to ruin your health. No one who does not ruin his health with study will ever do anything in chemistry nowadays.

If that was true of chemistry in the forties, how many hours a day would a man have to put in nowadays to master the science? But Kekulé managed to live to the age of sixty-seven and Liebig to the age of seventy, while their French contemporary, Chevreul, died at one hundred and three, so that chemistry need not be classed among the extra-hazardous occupations despite of long hours, poisonous fumes, and occasional explosions.

When Tyndall, in 1870, delivered his famous address on "The Scientific Use of the Imagination," unscientific people did not take him seriously, for they were accustomed to think of the imagination as the inventor of fiction, not as the guide to truth. They regarded it as a faculty for the manufacture of the mythology in which they delighted and they resented its employment for the advancement of the science which they despised. But the creative faculty is essentially the same whether it serves the purpose of the poet, the painter, the historian, the statesman, or the scientist.

To cite another instance let me quote from Henri Poincaré, one of the greatest of modern mathematicians and cousin of the President of France. When he was trying to work out the Fuchsian functions of the hypergeometric series—whatever they are—he tells us in his "Science and Method":

Naturally, I proposed to form all these functions. I laid siege to them systematically and captured all the outworks one after the other. There was one, however, which still held out, whose fall would carry with it that of the central fortress. But all my efforts were of no avail at first, except to make me better understand the difficulty, which was already something. All this work was perfectly conscious. Thereupon I left for Mont-Valérien, where I had to serve my time in the army, and so my mind was preoccupied with very different matters. One day, as I was crossing the street, the solution of the difficulty which had brought me to a standstill came to me all at once. I did not try to fathom it immediately, and it was only after my service was finished that I returned to the question. I had all the elements, and had only to assemble and arrange them. Accordingly I composed my definite treatise at a sitting and without any difficulty.

Another great mathematician, Sir William Rowan Hamilton, could likewise give the exact moment and spot when and where he made his most famous discovery, the new form of calculus called quaternions. His experience is as definite and vivid as the conversions we used to hear narrated at the old-fashioned prayer-meetings.

Quaternions started into life, or light, full grown, on Monday the 16th of October, 1843, as I was walking with Lady Hamilton to Dublin, and came up to Brougham Bridge, which my boys have since called the Quaternion Bridge. That is to say, I then and there felt the galvanic circuit of thought *close,* and the sparks which fell from it were the *fundamental equations between i, j, k; exactly such* as I have used them ever since. I pulled out on the spot a pocket-book, which still exists, and made an entry on which, *at the very moment,* I felt that it might be worth my while to expend the labour of at least ten (or it might be fifteen) years to come. But then it is fair to say that this was because I felt a *problem* to have been at that moment *solved*—an intellectual want relieved—which had *haunted* me for at least *fifteen years before. Less than an hour* elapsed before I had asked and obtained leave of the Council of the Royal Irish Academy, of which Society I was, at that time, the President—to *read* at the *next General*

Meeting a Paper on Quaternions; which I accordingly *did,* on November 13, 1843.

Hamilton also, I must mention, was noted for his power of thinking long and hard. Many times he sat at his mathematical work for more than twelve hours at a stretch; and, as Liebig said a scientist must, he ruined his health in the end by neglect of sleeping and eating.

Krapotkin, the prince of anarchists and a great geographer, relates a similar experience in his autobiography, ''The Memoirs of a Revolutionist'':

To discover the true leading principles in the disposition of the mountains of Asia—the harmony of mountain formation—now became a question which for years absorbed my attention. . . .

Beginning, then, with the beginning, in a purely inductive way, I collected all the barometrical observations of previous travelers, and from them calculated hundreds of altitudes, etc. . . . This preparatory work took me more than two years; and then followed months of intense thought, in order to find out what all the bewildering chaos of scattered observations meant, until one day, all of a sudden, the whole became clear and comprehensible, as if it were illuminated with a flash of light. . . .

There are not many joys in human life equal to the joy of the sudden birth of a generalization, illuminating the mind after a long period of patient research. What has seemed for years so chaotic, so contradictory, and so problematic takes at once its proper position within an harmonious whole.

To show how close this is to the use of the subconscious imagination in literary art we need only refer to what Stevenson, in his well known ''Chapter on Dreams,'' says of

My Brownies, God bless them! who do one-half my work for me while I am asleep and in all human likelihood do the rest for me as well, when I am wide awake and fondly supposing I do it myself.

It seems that he was particularly indebted to their aid in the theme of his most gruesome stories, ''Dr. Jekyll and Mr. Hyde'' and ''Olalla.'' Of the former he says:

I had long been trying to write a story on this subject, to find a body, a vehicle, for that strong sense of a man's double being which must at times come in upon and overwhelm the mind of every thinking creature. . . . Then came one of those financial fluctuations to which (with an elegant modesty) I have hitherto referred in the third person. For two days I went about racking my brains for a plot of any sort; and on the second night I dreamed the scene at the window, and a scene afterwards split in two in which Hyde, pursued for some crime, took the powder and underwent the change in the presence of his pursuers. All the rest I made awake, and consciously, although I think I can trace in much of it the manner of my Brownies. . . . The business of the powders, which so many have censured, is, I am relieved to say, not mine at all but the Brownies. Of another tale, in case the reader should have glanced at it, I may say a word; the not very defensible story of "Olalla." Here the court, the mother, the meetings on the stair, the broken window, the ugly scene of the bite, were all given me in bulk and detail as I have tried to write them; to this I have added only the external scenery (for in my dream I was never beyond the court), the portrait, the characters of Felipe and the priest, the moral, such as it is, and the last pages, such as, alas! they are.

It will be noticed that in all these cases, as in many others that might be cited, the revelation succeeds a period of intense and anxious thought on the problem to be solved. Then, when the strain of conscious attention has been relaxed, the solution comes spontaneously and seemingly from an external source. The idea may pop into one's mind as in the case of Poincaré when he is busy about something else or as in the case of Stevenson when he is asleep or as in the case of Kekulé when he is in a reverie. This last, sometimes called the hypnoidal state, seems to be peculiarly favorable to the evocation of fancies, whether factual or fictional, from the depths of the unconscious mind.

18

The War of Land and Sea

The world is losing ground. The land is slipping slowly into the sea. Water always runs downhill, and it always carries some of the hill with it, partly as sediment, partly as solution. However slowly a river may travel or however much it may meander, it reaches salt water in the end and brings along with it its own contribution of salts. What is carried back to the hills by the clouds and precipitated on the heights as rain is pure water, distilled water, evaporated from the surface of the sea by the sun, leaving behind all that it had dissolved as it streamed downward over the land.

Water is a universal solvent. It will dissolve anything, given enough of it. Even the royal metal gold that will stand boiling in concentrated nitric acid without perceptible loss can be dissolved in water. Sea-water contains a perceptible trace of gold, as it does of all the other elements.

"The waters wear away the stones," is true as Scripture. The gentlest stream will cut a channel for itself through the hardest rock in the course of time. The fretful waves dash perpetually against the cliff and are for ever thrown back in confusion. A losing battle? No, the fluid is constantly victorious over the solid in this eternal war of attrition, for every time the waves retreat they carry back with them some prisoner particles of the rock. So whether the cliff be chalk or basalt, whether the ocean attack in surf or ripples, the end is the same. The wall is worn away into ragged rocks and sand, and finally the sea flows over it in placid triumph.

The air aids the water in its fight for the reduction of the land to its own level. Here, too, we see an active fluid prevailing over a passive solid. The wind even drafts the earth particles into its service and with a sand-blast carves the rocks into grotesque and unstable shapes.

Sometimes, indeed, the soil is blown upward by the wind and may fall on higher ground, but gravitation is working all the time, while the wind opposes it only occasionally. The scales of nature are always weighted, and the balance must turn downward in the end.

Already the sea possesses nearly three fourths of the earth's surface. Is there enough room in the ocean to swallow up the rest of the land? Let us do a little figuring on it to see. The highest peak in the world is Mount Everest, so high that no man has ever yet reached its summit. Its height is 29,000 feet above the level of the sea.

The deepest known hole in the ocean bed is somewhere in the southeast Pacific. It is 32,114 feet below the level of the sea.

If then we were to pick up Mount Everest from off the roof of the world and drop it into this sub-sea-cellar, it would sink out of sight and would be covered by a half-mile of water! So, too, if we could by faith move all the mountains and cast them into the sea they would be quite lost.

But we should rather consider the mean level of land and sea than their extreme heights and depths. The ocean basins have an average depth of 12,000 feet below the sea-level. But the average elevation of all the continents is only 2300 feet above that plane. Then, since the sea area out-measures the land nearly three to one and since the sea is nearly five times as low as the land is high, the waters could cover the earth without any difficulty. If the earth were really "round like a ball," as we were taught it was, that is, if the earth were leveled to a perfect sphere, the water would stand two miles deep over the entire surface.

As Vachel Lindsay puts it in his "Sea Serpent Chantey":

> This is the voice of the sand
> (The sailors understand)
> There is far more sea than sand,
> There is far more sea than land.

Indeed there is; to be exact about it, seventy-two per cent of the earth's surface is covered with water. Of course "the sailors understand," and naturally they turn a deaf ear to the sigh of the sand over its lost territory. What alarms the sailors is the biblical prophecy that in the millennium "there shall be no more sea." But Kipling in "The Last Chantey" tells us that the Supreme Court reversed its ruling on this point and made an exception in favor of the "silly sailormen." Perhaps the silly sailormen would be no better satisfied with a world that was all ocean than with one that was all land.

Such a watery waste the earth probably was before the mountains were upthrust and such it may become again when they have been worn away. In the present intermediate period between these two diluvian ages land and sea are balanced and fluctuating. The solid crust of the earth, some sixty miles thick, rests upon a mobile mass of heated metal and rock. The mountains are made of lighter material than that which underlies the sea. That is why it has sunk and forms basins into which the salt water has gathered. But as the sediment brought down by the rivers gathers on the ocean bed it weighs it down still more, and at the same time the land is lightened of its load through the wearing away of the mountains. This necessitates a readjustment of the balance through the viscous substratum of the crust, and so the mountains rise a little, only to be gradually cut down again and cast into the sea.

But the net effect of all this fluctuation is to lower the land to the sea-level or below. Nature is the great leveler, and in this case, as in most, she levels down rather than up, if we view her operations from the standpoint of man, who is a land animal.

We may then foresee in the farthest future a greater deluge than that which Noah navigated, for it will not be limited to forty days, but will last until the seas freeze up solid or evaporate into space.

19

SCIENTIFIC FACTORS IN HISTORY

"The time has come," the Walrus said,
    "To talk of many things;
Of shoes—and ships—and sealing-wax—
    Of cabbages—and kings—"

With these cogent words the Rev. Charles Lutwidge Dodgson, of Oxford, the distinguished author of "An Elementary Treatise on Determinants with Their Application to Simultaneous Linear Equations and Algebraical Geometry," sounded the key-note of modern education.

A generation ago, when first uttered, this revolutionary doctrine was regarded as absurd. Historians for three thousand years had concerned themselves almost exclusively with two things, sealing-wax and kings, with legal documents and the doings of royalty, and neglected what is considerably more important and vastly more interesting, the life of the people, what they ate and what they wore and how they got about. The Assyriologist, digging in the ruins of a lost city, seizes upon a cuneiform tablet and eagerly breaks its seal only to meet in most cases with disappointment at finding it a court decision or a genealogy of the reigning family. The Egyptologist excavating a buried temple discovers upon its walls merely the record of a treaty or a eulogy of a Pharaoh. Doubtless these documents give as false an idea of the language and events of their time as our laws and treaties would of ours. An up-to-date archæologist would trade a treaty any day for a market report or give a dozen kings for a laundry list.

But by 1871, the date of the poem quoted above, it became obvious even to a walrus—which has the smallest brain of any mammal of its size—that the time had actually come to talk of many things hitherto ignored by chronicles, annals, monuments, memoirs, and state papers. Then arose a new school of historians who dug their material out of the garbage heaps of forgotten cities, sifting ashes, picking up bones, piecing together potsherds, scraping off pavements. Some casual simile in the Homeric poems turned out to be more valuable than the description of a battle, and the philosophical historians with a thesis to prove were less to be relied upon than gossipy globe-trotters like Herodotus, who just put down whatever interested him, good stories, queer customs, and every-day incidents.

The lives of the Cæsars may be useful to the alienist, but the true historian would rather have in equal detail the life of the most ignoble Roman of them all. There was only one Cæsar ordinarily, and it did not matter much how he behaved; but there were several million common people and their doings on the whole were more important than his. The raids of the northern barbarians are duly recorded, but no historian thought it worth while to mention the raids of the mosquitos, which had more to do with the depopulation of the Campagna than the Goths and Vandals. The historian of the future with a clearer idea of the real plagues of mankind will not talk so much about the Reign of Nero and the Age of Despots as he will about the Era of Malaria and the Hook-Worm Period.

The historian of the new school needs to have vastly more knowledge and ability than his predecessors. In order to put down what is most important he must first discover what is most important, no easy task even in contemporary history. Will the battle of the Marne and the Treaty of Versailles affect the future as much as the invention of the refrigerating machine and the dynamo? Who is the more important historical personage, George V or George Westinghouse? William II or William Marconi?

It is not sufficient nowadays for the historian to be an expert in paleography, philology, and archeology; he must also understand biology, geology, technology, and psychology. He must know everybody's business in order to know his own. He must haunt kitchens as well as court-rooms. He must keep an eye on the women and children. He must watch the weather and count the pigs and chickens. He is not interested in events but in the causes of events, differing in this respect from his predecessor, the annalist, who was incurious of causes and content to put down what happened.

The faults of the old historian were the same as the faults of modern journalists. He dealt with the unusual and therefore the less important things. He was like a grammarian who specified the exceptions but neglected to state the rule. He preferred to write of what he knew least about, of prodigies and miracles, of events remote in time or space. He tells of a freeze or flood but does not state the mean annual temperature and rainfall. He describes the distant landscape but does not say anything about the ground he is standing on. As Professor Robinson, one of the foremost advocates and practitioners of ''The New History,'' puts it:

In no other subject except history is fortuitous prominence accepted as a measure of importance. The teacher of chemistry does not confine himself to pretty experiments but conscientiously chooses those that are most typical and instructive. Metallic potassium and liquefied air are less common in the laboratory than water, lime and sulphuric acid. What would be the opinion in regard to a clinical lecturer who dwelt upon leprosy and the bubonic plague for fear his students might be bored by a description of the symptoms of measles and typhoid? In every study except history the teacher seeks to make the important and normal clear at any cost.

So the historian of the new school picks up such scattered fragments as he can and tries to piece together the life of past peoples. He still deals with the reigning dynasty, but he calls every monarch a pretender. He recognizes that the real ruler in all ages has been King Demos I. Therefore he is interested in the shoes he wore, the ships he voyaged in, the cabbages he cultivated. He has learned the lesson of the modern geologist, who is no longer so much concerned with catastrophic revolutions as with the effects of slow and imperceptible changes and who devotes himself to the study of such questions of climatology and evolution as

> When the sea was boiling hot
> And whether pigs had wings.

20

Do Two and Two Make Four?

If one hydrogen atom weighs 1.008, how much will four of them weigh? From what we have been taught at school we should answer 4.032, but it seems that this is wrong. For four hydrogen atoms go to make up one atom of helium, and that weighs just 4 and no more.

It is very disconcerting to have our simple childish faith in the solidity of matter upset in this way. Couldn't we have a law against teaching such as this that tends to undermine the fundamental dogma of the materialists?

But somehow the chemists, who are often accused of being materialistic, are quite tickled about the new notion and not a bit bothered by it, although it means giving up some of their long-cherished theories. The reason they don't mind changing their minds on this point is that the new theory explains something that has puzzled them for a hundred years.

In 1815 a man named Prout suggested that all the elements were made up out of the lightest element of them all, that is, hydrogen, just as all brick buildings, however different in shape and size, are made up out of brick of the same size. If so, all the atomic weights would be simple multiples of the atomic weight of hydrogen, and if that were taken as the unit, then all the atomic weights would come out handy whole numbers with no vulgar fractions left over. A scientist hates fractions as much as any school-boy. Carbon would then be just 12, oxygen would be just 16, and so on through the list. It was a fascinating idea and seemed likely, for most of the elements were pretty nearly whole multiples of hydrogen, and it was naturally suspected that the fractional atomic weight in the list might be due to erroneous determinations.

So the chemists set about the more exact determination of the weights of all the elements in the hope that they would come out nice and even. But it did not turn out as they hoped. On the contrary, the more careful they were with their weighing the more it became evident that hydrogen was not contained in the other elements an even number of times. It seemed, then, that Prout's hypothesis would have to be given up and that it could not be held that all the other elements were built up of hydrogen atoms.

For it was firmly believed up to the end of the nineteenth century that matter was indestructible, however much it might change its form. You can make carbon disappear, as you do when you burn coal in a grate, but if you should catch all the invisible gases that go up the chimney you would find that the carbon in the gases weighed just as much as the original coal. This was called the law of the conservation of mass. There was another law, the twin of this and regarded as equally absolute, the law of the conservation of energy, that energy also could neither be increased nor diminished although its form might be changed, as when we convert electrical energy into light and heat in the incandescent bulb.

The most exact weights and measurements confirmed these two laws. They do yet, for that matter. There is no direct experimental evidence to the contrary. But we do not nowadays regard them as so absolute as we used to suppose. We find apparent exceptions on both sides, and so we are coming to the conclusion that matter and energy are in some cases interchangeable. For instance, it is found that light, once regarded as wave motion in an immaterial ether, exerts a kick when it leaves a shining body and a push when it strikes an opaque body. Light, then, has inertia like matter. It seems to have weight, too, for Einstein has shown that a beam of starlight is attracted by the sun as it goes by.

In 1915, the centennial of Prout's hypothesis, Professor W. D. Harkins of the University of Chicago showed that after all the so-called atomic weights gave evidence in themselves that all *true* atomic weights are whole numbers, and this has become the famous whole-number rule upon which much of our modern atomic theory is now based. According to Harkins's theory all atoms are built of hydrogen, just as Prout supposed, but most of the hydrogen is first built into helium, in which process about 0.8 per cent of the mass seems to be lost but actually escapes as energy; and, surprising enough, the theory indicates that if one pound of hydrogen could be converted into helium, as seems to happen in the sun and the stars, as much heat would be given off as in the burning of ten thousand tons of coal, enough heat to warm a small dwelling for a thousand years.

This leads directly to the startling conclusion with which I began. For if the atomic weights of all the other elements are nice round numbers and if the atomic weight of hydrogen is such an odd number as 1.008, then something must be lost out somehow when the elements are built up out of hydrogen atoms. What is lost is, after all, just the 0.008 of the 1.008, which is thus converted into 1.000. Thus a free hydrogen atom weighs 1.008, but one which has been "packed" into another atom weighs only 1.000. This explains why four hydrogen atoms packed into helium weigh only 4, or sixteen in oxygen only 16. Thus chemists have their desire fulfilled, and all of the atomic weights other than that of hydrogen are whole numbers. Since the publication of Professor Harkins's whole-number rule it has been amply verified, for it has been proved by experiment that if only one kind of atoms, such as exist in carbon, or in one kind of chlorine, is taken, the atomic weight comes out just a whole number.

The importance of this may be brought out if we take a concrete case of such a size that we can grasp it. Let us suppose we are able to transmute hydrogen into oxygen on a large scale, although we are not yet able to do it even on a small scale. Let us fill a large glass flask with pure hydrogen. We will weigh into the flask sixteen and one eighth ounces of hydrogen and seal up the flask so that nothing can escape. Then we will set the reaction going; no matter how, for we do not know how. It would give a tremendous amount of heat and doubtless burst the flask or melt it, but we need not mind such little difficulties in an imaginary experiment. When all the hydrogen has been changed over into oxygen we will weigh the flask again and will find that its contents now weigh an even pound! What has become of the extra eighth of an ounce? The flask, we will assume, is tight. Nothing has got out of it but light and heat, which are not matter but energy, mere waves in the ether—if there is an ether.

It seems, then, that matter may be transmuted into energy and the reverse. If so, we shall have to combine the two laws of the conservation of mass and energy into one, since neither seems able to stand alone. This new view does not invalidate any of the old knowledge but brings us nearer to that unity of conception that is the aim of science. It is not a denial of matter any more than it is a denial of energy but enables us to understand better what they really are and how they are related. It explains many things that have puzzled us possibly more than that old problem of where the sun gets its heat. For the youngest stars consist mostly of hydrogen and the gas that is next to it in lightness, helium. The older stars that are cooling down like our sun contain heavier elements, like carbon and iron. Now, if these are formed from hydrogen in the process of cooling down, they must have enough heat to radiate for many million years.

On the other hand we have additional direct evidence in support of Prout's hypothesis that the elements are made out of hydrogen, for hydrogen has been got out of some of them. Sir Ernest Rutherford has found that he can get traces of hydrogen by bombarding another gas, such as nitrogen, with the swift and minute projections that are shot out from the radium atom. This upsets another old notion, that no element could be broken into other elements.

21

AN INVENTORY OF ENERGY

Our modern civilization has been developed by the lavish expenditure of the potential energy accumulated in the form of fossil fuel during geologic ages. Our wealth and industries, our comforts and luxuries, our science and art, our power and population, all are dependent upon the continuance of an adequate supply of energy from some source.

But the sources on which we are now relying—coal, oil, and gas—are being rapidly used up and are irreplaceable. Natural gas is almost exhausted. Gasolene production is about at its peak. Of coal the United States has enough for five thousand years, but many countries have not any.

It is high time the world took stock of all conceivable sources of mechanical power to determine how far civilization may be developed or how long it may be maintained at the present level. Such an inventory would require the coöperation of the scientists and engineers of all nations in an investigation lasting many years. But fortunately the means of such coöperation now exist for the first time in the International Research Council, which at Brussels in 1922 took under consideration this project. The question was also discussed at the Boston meeting of the American Association for the Advancement of Science in 1922, and a committee on photosynthesis was appointed.

Popular confidence that "science will find a way" before there is any serious shortage is flattering—but unfounded. If we try to list all the sources of energy that we can think of we will find that none of them is yet available or certain ever to be secured in adequate quantity.

Our primary and only practical source of energy is the sun. The sunshine falling upon a square mile of land at sea-level in our latitude in the course of a year is equivalent on the average to seven hundred thousand horse-power. To give us each the amount of energy we are now employing, one and a half horse-power, sixty square feet would be sufficient.

But no satisfactory solar engine has yet been discovered, and we are not able to make use of this abundant supply directly. Indirectly we can employ it in various ways. The heat of the sun causes currents in the air which we can use to propel sail-boats and run windmills. Doubtless wind-power can and will be used more in the future for both purposes, but the winds are variable and insufficient. The same may be said of the waves, and of the rise and fall of the tides, caused by the attraction of the sun and moon. Something may be done with them, but we must not expect too much.

The power that the sun provides continuously by pumping up water from the sea and depositing it upon the mountains in the form of rain can be used by damming up the streams and interposing turbines. We should make use of such water-power as rapidly and completely as possible to save our fossil fuel; but there is not enough of it in all the world to replace the coal consumed, and even in our favored land we could barely, by harnessing all the falling streams, get enough power to satisfy our present population, to say nothing of future needs.

Some day the world will have to stop drawing upon its carboniferous banks and live within its income. It will have to grow its fuel year by year as it grows its food. But it would be a great shock to civilization to have to shift back from coal and oil to the wood of two hundred years ago.

When we turn from the sun to the earth we find here also an abundance of power but no way to get it. We are living on top of a furnace, but fortunately for us the lid is thick and non-conducting. It has been often suggested that a hole might be bored down through the crust of the earth into the heated interior a few miles below, and through this water might be poured down, to come up steam. But this remains an engineering dream, though engines are run by internal heat in Italy, Hawaii, and California.

Last and most illusive of all is the internal energy of the atom, revealed to us in the heat that radium is continually giving off. We are using radium rays already to illuminate watch-dials and scorch out cancer. but many elements have similar stores of energy if we only knew how to release it. What it would mean if we should gain access to this exhaustless supply of potential wealth H. G. Wells has tried to tell in his romance, "The World Set Free," but even his brilliant imagination is baffled by its dazzling possibilities. So far scientists have not been able to unlock the atomic energy except by the employment of greater energy from another source.

Such in brief are our present situation and future prospects. The lesson is, first, that we should curtail the waste of our coal and oil, a loss to our country of a billion dollars a year, and, second, that we should start systematic research to develop new means of obtaining power such as a machine for converting the sunshine into electrical current.

CONCEIVABLE SOURCES OF ENERGY

I Non-solar
  1 Tides, lunar
  2 Internal heat of the earth
  3 Internal energy of the atom
II Solar
  1 Direct: Solar engines
  2 Indirect
   A Physical
    (1) Winds; by sails, windmills
    (2) Waterfalls; by water-wheels
    (3) Solar tides and waves
   B Chemical; oxidation of carbon and hydrogen
    (1) Internal; food
    (2) External; fuel
     a Gaseous; natural gas
     b Liquid; petroleum, vegetable oils, alcohol
     c Solid
      (a) Coal; ancient, limited
      (b) Wood; modern, continuous

22

THE FIGHT FOR THE FOOD AND FUEL OF THE FUTURE

The late unpleasantness was at first commonly called
the "European" war, but now we can see more clearly
that Europe was merely the battle-field.

To one born on the prairie, like myself, the cause of
the Great War is very plain. It was merely on a large
scale what he has seen on a small scale, the familiar
quarrel of the cattlemen with the sheepmen and of
the settler with them both. It was a symptom of the
passing of the open range. The Great War did not
begin in 1914, but in 1884 when Germany undertook
to put her brand on all the maverick territory in the
world. The war did not start on the Danube over the
body of the Austrian archduke, but in the Pacific
when Queensland quarreled with Germany over the
possession of New Guinea. Five years later we were
on the verge of a war with Germany over Samoa. In
Apia Harbor in 1889 three American war-ships con-
fronted three German war-ships with a British war-ship
in reserve, and only the intervention of a hurricane
prevented a naval battle. In Manila Bay in 1898 again
the American fleet was threatened by a superior German fleet, and again the British fleet stood by our side.
The attempt of Germany to stake out a claim in North
Africa was checked by the combination of England,
France, and Italy. Her attempt to get hold of Mesopo-
tamia and Persia was thwarted by the joint efforts of
England and Russia. This, you see, was the line-up

of the nine powers of the Great War, England, France, Italy, Russia, Japan, China, Belgium, Portugal, and the United States, against Germany. It was, as the German economists frankly stated, a fight for raw material. Germany wanted a "place in the sun," that is, tropical territory.

The reason for this sudden boom in the value of tropical real estate is because of two scientific discoveries, cheap transportation and cold storage. These have made dependencies as important as colonies. Formerly when the population increased the surplus had to emigrate, that is, to colonize. Now, thanks to refrigerated steam-ships, they can stay at home and have things brought to them. The old policy was to export people; the new policy is to import raw materials. Before the war England got sixty-five per cent of her essential foods from overseas. Germany got ninety per cent of her raw materials from the British Empire. It is cheaper for a Londoner to get a pound of butter from New Zealand than from Scotland. It is cheaper for a New Yorker to get a banana from Porto Rico than an apple from up-state.

The natural lines of traffic run north and south rather than east and west. Meridians of longitude are imaginary lines, as the geographies call them, but parallels of latitude mark real and ineradicable differences of climate and products. The temperate zone will be increasingly dependent upon the tropics for the necessities of life.

Where the sun strikes straightest and the rain falls heaviest there is the greatest wealth produced. A square mile of tropical land receives more energy from the sun than can be got from all the coal mined in the Rhine valley, and this perpetually and inexhaustibly. We cannot yet utilize this solar energy directly, but we can indirectly. Sugar is solidified sunshine. Oil is liquid sunshine. These two products contain nothing but the three elements, oxygen, carbon, and hydrogen, derived from the air and water and put together by the power of the sun's rays. When a tropical island sends off a ship-load of sugar or cocoanut-oil, it is losing nothing but what comes to it again freely. When a northern country sends off a ship-load of coal or petroleum, it is losing something that it can never replace.

It will not be long before the gasolene supply will be exhausted. Then we must fall back upon liquid fuel than we can raise, either alcohol or vegetable oils. But these can be produced most abundantly under tropical sunshine, and so we must look to the south for our future fuel unless we want to give up our automobiles, motor-boats, and airplanes and go back to the slow-coach days of the steam-engine. But the Diesel engine, the most efficient of the combustion engines, can be run on cottonseed-oil, peanut-oil, palm-oil, any old oil, as well as on petroleum. When Professor Diesel jumped off, fell off, or was pushed off the night boat from Holland shortly before the war, he was on his way to London to tell the English how by the use of their tropical territory they could remain masters of the seas even after the exhaustion of fossil fuel. Parliament has since made tropical oils a government monopoly so as to prevent them from falling again into

the hands of the Germans. We are now getting
margarin made from the coconut-oil from the Philippines and Samoa that formerly went to Germany.

No country can be called independent unless it has
command of the seven C's; namely, coffee, cotton, cane,
copra, cacao, and caout-chouc. The United States uses
three fourths of the world's rubber and does not grow
a pound of it. Nine tenths of the cultivated rubber is
raised on British plantations. We found out what that
meant during the war when rubber jumped to ten times
its former price and our automobile industry was
threatened with extinction. Yet we own the Philippines, where there is plenty of good rubber land.

The tropics are the richest part of the world in natural resources and the poorest in commercial wealth.
There lies the land that must produce the food and fuel
of the future.

23

YELLOW JOURNAL SCIENCE

Newspaper science is on the whole not so bad as it
is reputed to be in scientific circles. Statistical studies,
such as that carried out by Dr. Caldwell of the Lincoln
School, show that the papers publish a larger amount
of scientific information of a fair degree of accuracy
than is commonly recognized and that faking has mostly
gone out of fashion. The faults in the news section are
more often due to misinterpretation and misplaced em-
phasis than to intentional misconstruction.

But the pseudoscientific scare story is not yet extinct.

Its favorite field is a "pure food" campaign, being sometimes apparently instigated by a spirit of mere mischief and malice, sometimes obviously inspired by an opposing financial interest. It is easy to write an article that is wholly misleading yet contains no statement that can be denied. This is the style of it:

THERE IS DEATH IN THE POT![1]
A Chemical Compound Found in Many Articles of Food
TWO VIOLENT POISONS
Are United to Form This Adulteration

Chemical analyses carried on at the expense of this journal have disclosed the startling fact that many of our common articles of food contain large amounts of a chemical compound added under the pretense of preserving it and improving the taste. Most people do not even know the name of this substance, which is called by some chemists sodium chloride, although it is not certain what it really is, for cyclopedias we have consulted assert that it is muriate of soda. However, it is bad enough whichever is right. Sodium chloride is a mineral occurring in many parts of the earth, and the spots where it is abundant are distinguished by the destruction of all vegetation, which shows its poisonous nature. It is contained in sea-water to the extent of two and a half per cent, and it is this which makes sea-water impossible to drink. As we all know, persons immersed in sea-water die in a few minutes, and many are made deathly sick by merely being conveyed over it in ships.

One of the constituents of this drug is a metal known to chemists as sodium, which on being thrown on water decomposes it with a violent explosion. It is so poisonous that a piece of the size of a pea placed on the tongue of a dog will kill a man. The other ingredient, chlorine, is a greenish-yellow gas of so suffocating a character that it attacks the

[1] From "The Daily Jaundice," 'most any day.

throat and lungs in a most painful manner if inhaled in the slightest quantity and causes death in a few minutes if continued. This is the poison gas used by the Germans at Ypres.

All the chemists we have interviewed agree as to the deadly character of these two elements, but some assert that by combining the two the resulting compound becomes innocuous. We give this theory for what it is worth, and if our readers can swallow such stuff, they may. We would, however, advise any one who accepts this hypothesis, that two poisons are better than one, to try a mixture of strychnine and arsenic, which on this theory ought to be perfectly harmless.

The financial side to this question is hardly less important than the hygienic. Sodium chloride is very cheap, and so every pound of it that can be added to marketable food means so much more profit to the unscrupulous manufacturer. On our first page is a graphical diagram in black and red, showing the extent of the pernicious practice. Take, for instance, a few common articles of food and figure it out for yourself:

	Percentage of sodium chloride	Selling price per hundred pounds	STEAL
Codfish	17	$30.00	$5.80
Bacon	5	25.00	1.25
Butter	6	55.00	3.30
Dried beef	10	80.00	8.00

When a man can buy a crude drug at a cent a pound and sell it at eighty cents a pound as food to the unsuspecting public, it indicates that there is something putrefying in the Danish kingdom, as Shakspere says.

None of the chemists seen by our reporter dared deny the extensive use of sodium chloride in food, without any warning of its presence being given to the purchaser, although they all affected to consider the matter of slight importance. We shall see if the people will agree with them as to this. We have witnesses to prove that tons of this stuff were added by avaricious corporations to the meats shipped overseas to our brave boys fighting for freedom and democracy.

There is only one way to stop this growing evil, and that

is by prompt and efficient legislation. It would not be fair to prohibit the use of sodium chloride entirely and suddenly. No, let those who want their food mixed with a poisonous metal and a suffocating gas have it so by all means. It will save the fool-killer some trouble. But let the innocent public be protected. A law embracing the following points would undoubtedly be effective:

First, put a tax of ten cents a pound on all foods containing this chemical.

Second, require a license of $200 to $500 from every dealer selling food adulterated in this way, and prohibit the selling of any other kinds of food in the same shop.

Third, all articles of food containing this drug must be colored green with some harmless coloring matter. This would be perfectly fair, because it would not interfere with the flavor of the food, yet would prevent the deception of any one eating it.

Fourth, every hotel, restaurant, or boarding-house using such food should be required to post in conspicuous place a placard with the words, "Adulterated food used here," in letters not less than one inch square.

Laws embodying these provisions have already been adopted in several of the States against oleomargarin and similar frauds, and have accomplished their purpose of destroying the traffic without in the least interfering with the liberty of the individual.

When we think of the luxury of our robber princes, which was so vividly depicted in our recent articles on "A Billion Dollar Wedding" and "The Funeral of a Multimillionaire," and whose splendor, pleasures, and vices are alike founded on the sweat of the working-man, who buys at an extravagant price this chemical, and with it attempts to satisfy the hunger of his starving wife and children, who ask for bread and get a stone, since sodium chloride is properly classed in the mineral kingdom, and is therefore unsuited for human food, as is shown by the fact that it is at once excreted from the body even in tears, then it is time to call a halt and ask, Whither are we drifting?

24

Byron's Blunders

Ridicule is the handiest weapon for knocking a new idea on the head, and it is often effective. Yet sometimes the idea may survive or in later times revive, and then the ridiculer becomes ridiculous.

A curious instance of this is the attempt of Lord Byron to laugh out of life certain infant ideas that were beginning to attract attention in his time.

In his outburst of poetic spleen, "English Bards and Scotch Reviewers," he undertakes to expose four popular fallacies in four lines:

> What varied wonders tempt us as we pass!
> The cowpox, tractors, galvanism and gas,
> In turns appear, to make the vulgar stare,
> Till the swollen bubble bursts and all is air!

Lord Byron, being above the vulgar throng, was not to be taken in by such nonsensical ideas and pointed out that they were mere passing fads.

Yet, somehow, they did not turn out to be altogether hot air but have settled down into sober science. In the cowpox inoculation we see the beginning of a new era in medicine in which diseases were to be fought with nature's own antidotes, the first attempt to attack a specific malady with a specific preventative. To-day we have many cases where the physician can hit directly at an invading virus with a counteractant. But opponents of vaccination still survive, although smallpox, thanks to vaccination, has become largely extinct.

What Byron called tractors have long since gone out of fashion. Even the word is now applied to something much more recent. Tractors then were apparatus used to fix the attention of men and women and throw them into a sort of trance. This is what we now call hypnotism. It has been shorn of its early eccentricities and extravagancies and is now admitted to the most respectable of psychologies. Its fundamental principle, autosuggestion, has been found to be the key to many a mental mystery.

What galvanism has done for the world we all know. The galvanic cell is part of our daily life, and we could hardly do without it. It runs our electric automobiles and door-bells, our telegraphs and telephones. It produces the soap and bleaching powder that clean our clothes.

What a chorus of laughter greeted the suggestion that London might be lighted by coal-gas! Sir Walter Scott wrote in a letter: "There is a madman here proposing to light London with smoke." Napoleon, who usually turned a kindly ear to scientific novelties, said it was *une grande folie*. Anybody with common sense could see that it was absurd to think of lighting a city with something that could not be seen, felt, or weighed.

Yet gas came in and illuminated our lives for a hundred years until it was superseded by something still more intangible, electricity, which could not even be smelled. Although gas has now gone rather out of fashion as an illuminant, it is being used more than ever as a fuel and may in time displace the heavy and dirty lumps of coal in power-plants and homes.

These were the four permanent contributions of

science to civilization which Byron picked out as follies of the day soon to be exploded. As old De Morgan said in his fascinating "Bundle of Paradoxes," "It was hard lines to select four candidates for oblivion not one of whom got there."

But before you get too contemptuous of Byron see if you are any better in the valuation of contemporary achievement. Write down four ideas and innovations of the present day that you regard as bubbles that will soon burst and four that you think will persist and grow in importance. Put your prophecies in an envelope and place it in the hands of your children or a library to be opened in 2022. At that time you will either be hailed as a wonderful prophet or be made the text of a screed like this.

What we should learn from Byron's blunder is not credulity, not incredulity, not that intermediate and lazy state of mind which says of every novelty, There seems to be something in it. Our mental attitude should be that of skepticism; not in its modern meaning of distrust but in its original sense of examination. When the Greeks invented the term "skeptic" they meant a man who used his eyes to look into things, not one who shut his eyes to any innovation.

25

THE POPOVER STARS

In the Washington hotels they have a curious custom. A negro boy wanders about the dining-room with a

curious tin box slung from his shoulders. When I saw
him first passing from table to table and holding out the
box to each diner in turn I thought he was collecting
contributions for the Armenians or Chinese or some
other sufferers, and I felt in my pocket for the smallest
coin that would rattle satisfactorily. But when he
came to me he opened the tin contraption, and I saw
that I was expected to take out something instead of
to put in something. I stuck in my hand and pulled
out a popover. A popover is a kind of hollow-hearted
muffin. It is very light, and one can eat a lot of them
without getting enough calories to upset his trial
balance, and, what's a wonder, they are not charged
for on the bill, no matter how often the boy with the
hat-box comes around or how many you take at a time.
The popover is constructed on the model of a dirigible,
a thin silky shell blown out from the inside by some
hot gas.

While I was ruminating over the popover I was
struck by its resemblance to the giant stars that I had
been reading about. These, like the popover, are not
so substantial as they seem, for they, too, are puffed
out by some internal expansive agency. But these stars
have not any crust like the popovers and their dough
is not sticky, so that the puzzle is to find out why they
do not either fly to pieces or fall together.

For instance, consider the big red star that the
astronomers know as Betelgeuse in Orion, but which
the vulgar call "Beetlejuice in O'Ryan." If you need
an introduction to Betelgeuse ask your grandmother
to point him out to you. For in her day every respectable person was supposed to know the names of

the constellations and the cabinet officers. The younger generation does not seem to care about either. But however indifferent you may be to the heavenly bodies, you probably can recognize at sight two constellations, the Big Dipper and the three stars that form the Belt of Orion. Now, Betelgeuse is the Alpha or leading star in Orion and lies in the giant's shoulder, so that you can find it even though you may not have a grandmother handy to use as a star-finder.

When Betelgeuse was measured on Mount Wilson by means of Michelson's interferometer in 1920 it was found to be about 250,000,000 miles in diameter, almost big enough to fill the orbit of Mars and allow the earth, Venus, and Mercury to travel around their regular orbits inside. Perhaps our sun was about that size in its younger and stronger days before Mars had seceded and established its independence. But since then the sun has shrunk so that it would take about thirty million suns to fill up Betelgeuse.

And then there is a bright star in the Scorpion, so red that the Greeks named it Antares, the antagonist of Mars; but they are not to be compared in bulk, for Antares is about four hundred million miles in diameter and therefore about seventy million times larger in volume than our sun.

But we must not allow ourselves to be overawed by the red giants. They are bigger than the mind of man may conceive, but they are not so substantial as the body of man. The density of the sun is only a quarter of the density of the earth, but these stars are more tenuous still. They are merely giant gas-bags—minus the bag. They are lighter than air, in some cases a

HOW THE GIANT STARS WERE MEASURED

Upper end of the tube of the 100-inch Hooker telescope of the Mount Wilson Observatory of the Carnegie Institution of Washington, showing the 20-foot Michelson interferometer. This attachment to the telescope is used to measure with high precision the angular distance between the components of double stars, so close that even in the largest telescopes they appear as single stars; and also the diameters of stars.

Pencils of light from each of the stars (or from two halves of the single disk in case of measurement of diameter) are received by the small flat mirrors near the ends of the beam and are reflected, parallel to the beam, to a second pair of mirrors near the middle, which throw them down the tube to the large mirror, whence they are reflected into an eye-piece and brought into coincidence. The end of the tube is covered so that no other light can enter the telescope. When properly adjusted, the two pencils from each star "interfere," thus forming a series of alternately bright and dark fringes which cross the image of the star. Each component of the double star has its own system of interference fringes, whose relative position in the eye-piece depends upon the distance separating the stars and the distance between the outer pair of mirrors mounted upon the beam. By varying the separation of the mirrors, a distance can be found for which the bright fringes of one set fall on the dark fringes of the other set. The entire system of fringes then disappears, and the image is uniformly illuminated. The angular distance separating the stars (or the diameter of a single star) is easily calculated when the distance between the mirrors corresponding to a disappearance of the fringes is known.

In the case of Betelgeuse the fringes disappear when the outer mirrors are ten feet apart and from this it is calculated that the star measures about 250,000,000 miles across and is some thirty million times the size of our sun. Betelgeuse as observed from the earth seems the same size as a plate, one foot in diameter, seen from a distance of about 800 miles.

thousand times lighter, more like what we call a vacuum.

Our wise youngsters will not be content with the rimes of old Mother Goose but will demand a new version something like this:

> Twinkle, twinkle, giant star,
> I know exactly what you are,
> An incandescent ball of gas
> Condensing to a solid mass.

> Twinkle, twinkle, giant star,
> I need not wonder what you are,
> For seen by spectroscopic ken
> You're helium and hydrogen.

For the stars reverse the rules of plants and animals. They grow smaller as they grow older. The red giants are the infants of the stellar world. As they settle down they shrink.

On the start the stars are reduced to their elements; more than that, for the elements themselves are reduced to their electrical components, the protons and electrons, mere fragments of atoms. The attraction of gravitation acts upon these flying particles, keeping them together in great gaseous globes and drawing them together with smaller solid spheres.

Here the question naturally arises, why do not the particles come together at once? Why do they stay up (that is, out) instead of falling down (that is, in)? Why do the giant stars remain so swollen for untold millions of years? Gravity is all the time pulling the particles to a common center. What force keeps them apart?

The answer that is now given to this question would have been thought ridiculous to a former generation. For the answer is that the stars are kept swollen out by the pressure of the light inside of them.

Now, we did not use to think of light's exerting any pressure, for we could not conceive of light's having anything like weight, inertia, or momentum. For these were properties of matter, and light was classed with heat and electric radiations as energy. In those days —away back in the last century—a very strict line was drawn between matter and energy. But now we know that when a sunbeam strikes the earth it gives it a push just as dropping a stone on it does. The force of the impact of light rays is infinitesimal, but upon such minute particles as make up the giant stars it must have a perceptible effect. The radiant energy from the outer layers of the star streams off unrestricted into empty space. A beam of it may reach our earth after several centuries of travel. But the light and heat from the interior parts of the star, radiating straightaway in all directions, cannot get out so easily; for the ray strikes against the particles above and is driven back in a new direction, only to run up against another particle and be again deflected. In the course of time, hundreds of years perhaps, the imprisoned ray may find its way out of the maze, since there is plenty of space between the particles of the gaseous star, but only after many rebuffs. The rays at such high temperatures as the stars are of very high frequency of vibration, more like the X-rays, which will lose half their power in penetrating a distance of eight inches through the air. So if the star has the density of air the rays would generally get tired out before they have gone many inches.

But every time a ray is turned back it gives a kick to the particle that checked it on its outward way. These accumulated kicks keep the particles from crowding in to the center as fast as they otherwise might. It is as if a strong hot wind were blowing outward from within the star. The heat comes from within, not from without as with the popovers in the oven. The source of the heat is surmised to be formation of heavier atoms than the primeval hydrogen.

It is only as the radiant light and heat escape into outer space that the particles, freed from its interference, can settle down comfortably together and cool off. But this takes a long time, for the radiation in attempting to escape has set the particles into more rapid motion; and as they draw nearer together they jostle one another more frequently, and this increases their agitation. So a gaseous star at first gets hotter as it contracts, its temperature rising from 3000 to 10,000 degrees centigrade and its color changing from red to blue. Then as it loses heat it shrinks and solidifies and runs back to red and finally becomes black and cold.

Our Sun must be classed as a late yellow dwarf, though that sounds like a variety of pea. He is gradually becoming redder in the face, but it is the rubicund visage of old age, not the rosy flush of youth.

But let us not be ashamed of our little old Sun. If we measure by mass instead of mere girth he can stand comparison with any of the starry host. He is not so puffed up as the younger stars, but he has more solidity and amounts to about as much on the whole. Even the heaviest and hottest of the stars, the bluish-white helium giants, are none more than eighteen times the mass of the sun, and some of the stars we see have less than a tenth of the sun's weight. It is better for us to have a sun that is in the cooling-off than in the heating-up stage, and it will be many millions of years before we need order our furs for an Eskimo existence to the end of time.

26

Soda-Water

When you are hot and tired from a long walk you naturally drop into the nearest drug-store and take a seat on the wire-legged stool before the marble monument and say to the young man in the apron, "Plain soda, please." Natural enough it is. But funny when you think of it. For what you are paying for is the very thing that you are most anxious to get rid of. What you suck in through the straw is just what you expel with every panting breath.

For soda-water does not contain soda. This is one of these misbrandings that the law allows because it can't stop its use. It is a hang-over word, like "sardines" that never saw Sardinia and "bologna" that does not come from Italy.

Soda-water used to be made from baking-soda by the action of some acid that releases the desired gas. Then limestone was substituted for soda because it was cheaper and just as good. But the thirst of young America seemed likely to melt away mountains of marble, and so it is now customary to catch and compress the gas that escapes from soda-springs or from the fermenting vats of beer or near-beer or from the combustion of coal.

What soda-water is composed of you may see for yourself if you watch your glass as it stands on the table after you have slaked your first thirst. You will see that it is separating into two different things, a liquid and a gas. The liquid is plain water as you will find out if you are too slow about drinking. The other is a heavy gas that slips up through the water in little bubbles and collects in the empty half of the tumbler. This gas is as invisible as air, but you can prove that it is not air by striking one of the matches on the table before you and plunging it into the upper part of the glass. You will see that the light will be put out before it reaches the water. The gas is so heavy that you can fairly drink it from the glass, and it has, as you know, a tingle-tangle taste. It is also slightly sour, or, as the chemist would call it, a weak acid. "Carbonic acid" is the old name for it, but it is more correct to name it, when it is out of the water, "carbon dioxide."

Into these two things then, water and carbon dioxide, your plain soda dissolves before your eyes. The remarkable thing about it is that all living beings are dissolving into these same two things, also before your eyes, though you do not see it.

Every plant from the yeast to the pine, every animal from a midget to a man, is continually being converted into water and carbon dioxide and passing off in a gaseous form.

While you are musing over it, your glass of soda-water is slowly evaporating. So are you. And into the same elements. You can prove this without leaving your chair. Wipe one side of the tumbler dry with your paper napkin and breathe against the cold glass. There is the dew into which you are dissolving.

The other product of your internal combustion, carbon dioxide, you can identify if you will ask the clerk on the other side of the drug-store to pour you out a glass of lime-water. Stick your straw into it but blow instead of sucking. You will see the water turn milky—a common trick of the amateur magician and a proof of the presence of carbon dioxide. This white sediment is the same substance as the original limestone from which the carbon dioxide may have been derived.

You are therefore gradually becoming gasified, and the end-products of your life-reaction are water and carbon dioxide. We may measure your vitality by weighing these products of your activity. If you are leading the sedentary life, your output of soda-water will be low. If you are leading the strenuous life, it will be high.

When you are working hard, say sawing wood or riding a bicycle uphill, you may be exhaling as much as five ounces of carbon dioxide in an hour. When you are sitting still you are exhaling about an ounce.

Food and fuel, the source of animate and inanimate energy, whatever runs our engines or our bodies, all turn out as soda-water in the end. The furnace cannot consume its own smoke in the place of fresh fuel. We must turn over this useless product, soda-water, to the green leaves; for they, under the stimulus of sunshine, have the power to reverse this reaction, to release the oxygen again to the air, and to store up the carbon and hydrogen as food or fuel. In this form they are once more at the disposal of man to furnish him strength to do his work.

So that Yankee ingenuity has converted this waste product of all life into a reinvigorator.

This glass of plain soda is not so plain as it seems at first sight. There is more to be got out of it than the man at the fountain put into it.

Why does the gas escape from the liquid? Because the liquid has more gas than it has a legal right to hold. There are two laws regulating this matter. One says that the higher the temperature the less the gas that can be dissolved in a liquid. Your glass of water can hold easily two glassfuls of carbon dioxide when it is ice-cold but only one glassful at the temperature of the room. Since the soda-water as it stands is warming, it must give off half of its gas.

The other law is that the greater the pressure the more gas will be dissolved in a given quantity of water. Under ordinary conditions a pint of water will hold about a pint of gas. Making the pressure four times as great, it will dissolve four pints. If you will call this fact "Henry's law" you will have a higher appreciation of the value of the information. The reason why soda-water is so nice is because you get more for your money than you think you are getting. If you pay a nickel for a pint you get five pints of fluid —only a cent a pint. It is consequently very filling and satisfying to the thirsty soul, who, like all human beings, wants so much more than he can hold.

The imprisoned gas, when the pressure is removed by the pulling of a cork or the running from the fountain, tries to escape, and it is very interesting to watch its struggles in your glass. The gas that is dissolved in the water at the surface can go right off into the air, but that which is down deeper has a harder time. The little individual bubbles clinging to the side and bottom are too weak individually to push their way through the water to the top. Then the era of merger begins. Several little bubbles join together and form a syndicate. This draws to it all the little bubbles near it and absorbs them. Some of the bubbles you will see trying to preserve a quasi-independence as they cling together, but the filmy partition finally breaks. The trust is formed and soars upward, growing as it goes. There are two reasons why it gets bigger as it rises through the water: one is that the pressure gets less, as with a balloon in the air, and the other is that the gas in the water through which it passes can escape into it as easily as from the surface above.

"Unto him that hath shall be given," is also a physical law. As the bubble gets bigger the pressure holding it in gets weaker, just as when you blow up a circus balloon or one of those inflating squawkers that the children have. You have to blow hard at first, but as the rubber film expands it becomes weaker, and you have to look out or you will burst it with your breath. Now, the bubble of gas in the water is held together by just such an elastic film. You used to call this force "capillary attraction," but you must say "surface tension" or "interfacial energy" nowadays, or else your children will laugh at you.

As the bubbles get bigger, then, the surface tension gets weaker, because it is less arched. It is a poor rule that will not work both ways. All scientific laws should be good rules. Conversely, then, let us say, that the smaller the bubble the greater the force necessary to expand it. That is all right for a way, but if you work it back mathematically to its extreme limit you will reach the absurd conclusion that no bubble can have ever been begun. Or to put it in another way, if the bubble is next to nothing in size it will be next to impossible to start it. The scientists, however, are not at all embarrassed by such a reduction to absurdity. If a law does not go their way they part company with it without a pang. In this case they simply say the rule does not apply to infinitesimal bubbles, which is obviously true.

But you can see for yourself that, even if it is not impossible, it is very difficult for a bubble to get a start in life. The bubbles begin on the sides and bottom of the glass where there is some little irregularity in the surface to give them a chance. If there is a little scratch made by careless scouring of the glass you will find them lined up along that. A glass with a perfectly smooth, even surface will retain the gas much longer. Champagne glasses have a deep, hollow stem from which the bubbles stream up for a long time, so that the liquor will keep "alive" longer. Stir your soda with a straw and see the bubbles rise.

If you don't want the big trust bubbles to rise to the top and escape with their accumulations, thicken the water with some sugar syrup from the other faucet of the fountain, and then the bubbles will accumulate on top in a rosy mass of foam and froth, very pretty, but not good for anything.

But this philosophizing makes one thirsty. Our soda-water is getting stale from standing. All the life is going into the foam. Blow it off and drink.

27

THE CULTIVATION OF OBLIVIOUSNESS

The art of seeing things is one which educators have always commended and tried to train, but the city man needs nowadays to learn how not to see things. Our streets are turned at night into continuous Fourth of July celebrations wherein electric fireworks flare and flash and flame. Glow-worms crawl up and down the front of the buildings. Zigzag lightning strikes a sign-board. Words are spelled out letter by letter or written with an invisible pen or race across the sky-line of a block. Fiery highballs are continually compounded. Bottles pour out a ceaseless flood of sparkling beverage. A mammoth squirrel runs unweariedly in his whirling cage. A four-story Highlander dances flings eternally. A gigantic kitten plays with a Ferris-wheel spool and then leaps with one bound to the top of a sky-scraper. An eagle, the size of Sindbad's roc, flaps its wings and soars aloft and then returns to roost.

Amid all this glare and flare and flicker the weary workman plods his homeward way, thinking of naught but supper. The pleasure-seekers thread their way through the maze in complete unconsciousness of the rainbow lights on every side. They might not be able to tell you the name of a single one of the signs which have been flashed upon them. They have looked at them but not perceived them. They have seen them only to shut them out of their inner sight. They have found it necessary thus to blind their conscious vision in order to attend to their own affairs. The failure to cultivate obliviousness may involve the penalty of death. The automobiles show no mercy to the startled stranger who stops an instant in the midst of the street to look at a *Ben-Hur* chariot-race.

The mental mechanism by which these sights are shunted off must be a curious thing. It is perhaps the same as the Freudian censor who shields the self from unpleasant thoughts, a sort of office-boy who keeps unwelcome visitors from bothering the boss. And so the struggle goes on incessantly between the advertiser who is trying to attract our attention and the guardian of the gate whose business it is to keep our attention from being distracted. In this contest the ultimate victory lies with the defense. To dazzle our eyes is to blind them, and the sign-board that we are at first forced to see becomes the easiest to avoid in the future. The consciousness becomes callous, and we are protected from further disturbance by a sort of induration of the intellect. So it comes that the city man pays no more attention to a tungsten film in nitrogen or a cascade of colored lights than the countryman pays to Venus in the heavens or the fireflies in the grass.

28

How a Chemist Tricked His Wife

Food conservation would be easier if food conservatism were not so great. The public is quite suspicious of any food in which the chemist has been concerned, and the popular prejudice is not without reason, as we must confess when we think how often he has lent his skill to the unscrupulous manufacturer to make a poor product look better than it should.

The war jolted us out of our ruts a bit in this respect as in others. Under the combined motives of patriotism and economy many people took to synthetic butters who hitherto had refused to taste of anything other than that prepared from the fluid extract of Vacca. But dietary habits are hard to break, and so it is usually necessary to resort to camouflage in introducing a new food. After the housewife has been won over, the conservatism of the servant has still to be surmounted. In one case that I know of the attempted introduction of margarin into the household caused the cook to leave. She had never worked in a family where they did such things, and she wasn't going to, so there. The mistress accepted her resignation and got another girl to whom she carefully explained that margarin was a pure vegetable compound, free from the tuberculosis germs that sometimes come in butter and considerably cheaper. The new cook listened attentively and said "Yesm'm." Henceforth margarin was duly served at the dinner-table, but when the bills came in the mistress discovered that her cook had been buying gilt-edged butter at fifty-five cents a pound for her own eating in the kitchen.

A professor of chemistry in the University of Atlantis suggested to his wife that she try one of the new butter substitutes which he had analyzed and found to be satisfactory. She did not receive the suggestion enthusiastically though he often referred to the subject and tried to convert her to his view. But women are naturally conservative, and wives do not always pay as much attention to the opinions of their husbands as they should even when their husbands are scientists. So he made up his mind to trick her into trying it. He bought a pound of margarin and stole some annatto to color it. I should explain that he is ordinarily an honest man and never steals unless he has to. This time he had to, for the laws of the State forbid the grocer to sell or give away any coloring-matter with margarin, but he keeps a box of annatto capsules on the counter and if customers help themselves he never calls a policeman.

Well, the chemist came home while his wife was working with the other ladies of the faculty at Red Cross supplies; and, taking out the pat of butter from the ice-box, he tinted and salted and shaped the margarin till it looked and tasted just like what was in the butter-dish.

That evening he watched his wife narrowly as she buttered her bread and potatoes but she did not seem to notice the difference. When dinner was over he asked her if she noticed anything peculiar about the butter. She said she did not. Then he laughed in the harsh and unfeeling way of husbands who get a joke on their wives, and said, "That's margarin you've been eating!"

"I know it," his wife replied calmly. "We've had nothing else in the house for the last three weeks."

29

What Is the Matter With the Artists?

The most common remark to be overheard at an exhibition of ultra-modern art is, "Why, these artists must be crazy!"

Now to call another man "crazy" is not enlightening. It is too easy and explains nothing. Besides, each one of us thinks those who differ from us in opinion, and especially in taste, are a bit wrong in the head.

"All the world is queer, except thee and me," said the old Quaker to his wife, "and sometimes I think thee is a little queer."

We are not all so frank as the Quaker, even to our wives, but I suspect we feel much the same way about the world.

But if, instead of recklessly applying the word "crazy" to everything we do not like or understand, we should analyze ourselves to find what is the reason, or rather the cause, of our instinctive repugnance, it might be helpful to us. It may be that we hate the new thing merely because it is new. If so, we may say that we are merely suffering from neophobia. Giving a complaint a Greek name is a great consolation, as every physician knows.

Or we may set a psychological expert to analyzing the people who are disturbing our minds by their unconventional notions and so find out why they show such strange tastes. Dr. Stewart Paton, lecturer on psychiatry at Columbia University, has made such an analysis of modern art in his new book, "Signs of Sanity," and has come to the following conclusion:

The futurist art expresses, not intellectual superiority, but very primitive emotion, and illustrates a reversion to ideas and ideals of the Stone Age. It is not what its devotees claim for it, the product of conscious intellectualization of the creative spirit. The futurist, like a good many other people who are trying to find some compensation for defects in their personality, instead of being an interpreter of new sensations and emotions, is expressing those that were more characteristic of man during the early periods of his history than they are of human beings to-day. The literary, as well as musical moderns, in their unsuccessful efforts to find new and startling lines of expression, have practically only succeeded in recalling some forgotten memories of very primitive ancestors. The futurists practically depend for their inspiration upon the revival of subconscious mental activities that extend far back in the history of the race, and they surrender unconsciously to the primitive vision and emotions of an almost forgotten past. Their philosophy of art is based almost entirely upon illusion and fallacy; for instead of listening to reason, they have simply succeeded in giving expression to very primitive tendencies that have been successfully inhibited by the real intellectuals who have contributed to the progress of civilization. It is of great assistance in preserving our sanity to have some appreciation of the nature and genesis of these primitive impulses and not to make the mistake of believing them to be evidences of intellectuality.

This explains why successive waves of fads in art, each more extravagant than the last, have swept over the world, and it shows their connection with other signs of the times. The recrudescence of superstition, the revival of race hatreds, the growth of belligerency, the glorification of brutality, the defiance of law, the contempt for intellectuality, the prevailing tendencies in music, dancing, literature, and dress, as well as in painting and sculpture, all indicate a reversion to that primitive psychology which arose out of the war, or out of which the war arose. The Pre-Raphaelite movement of the last century has become the Pre-Troglodyte movement of the present century. Young artists who used to go to Paris or Rome for study now seek inspiration in Tahiti or the Congo.

But while recognizing the fact that futuristic art points backward we may continue to admire it or be amused by it, according to our taste. A dip into the primitive or a flight into the unconventional may not be a bad thing for us once in a while. It will keep us from getting stuck in the mud.

But if it should become epidemic and chronic—then, good-by, civilization.

30

How Man Got His Shoe

According to the Oriental tale, all men went barefoot in the old days, for they knew nothing of shoes. The soles of the people were hardened to walk upon the ground, but the king's feet were tender, for wherever he walked carpets were spread before him. This arrangement was considered mutually satisfactory, or rather was not considered at all, being regarded as natural and therefore inevitable. But one day a new bride was brought to the king, the loveliest lady in all the land, and a long strip of carpet was laid from the palace steps to the highway so that the king could go forth to meet her. As evidence of the truth of the tale you may still see such a carpet laid in front of a building where there is a wedding.

As the bridal cortège approached, the king marched majestically down the carpeted pathway to the end where he was to await his prospective bride. But when he caught sight of her riding on her palfrey he found her more beautiful than his courtiers had said she was (this is the most incredible thing in the story) and, carried away by passion, rushed forward to greet her.

But just as soon as the tenderfoot king stepped on the ground his soft sole was cut by a sharp-edged flint, so that when the princess first saw her royal bridegroom he was holding one foot in his hand and howling.

The king, feeling doubly sore from the wound and the humiliation, at once called together the wise men and the soothsayers and astrologers and ordered them under pain of beheading to devise means of carpeting the whole earth so that wherever he trod no such accident should ever happen again. The official board of experts flunked this intelligence test as usual. I mean, as usual in Oriental tales. They first scratched their heads and then shook them and were likely in the end to lose them. They figured out that there was not enough material of any sort to cover the whole earth and reported to the king that his demand was mathematically impossible.

But the king was inexorable and gave them twenty-four hours to solve the problem. At the twenty-third hour the situation was saved by a poor maker of leather aprons, who appeared before the king, and, kneeling at his feet, put on them two queer-looking contraptions. Then he asked the king to walk out upon the highway and the fields and see if the earth was not carpeted wherever he walked.

The king tried it and found that it was as he had been told. Overjoyed at this happy solution of the difficulty, he offered the poor leather-worker half of his kingdom and his daughter in marriage. But the leather-worker declined both with thanks and asked instead that he be allowed to extend the benefits of his new invention to all the people. The king generously granted his request and issued an edict that everybody should be shod with the new pedal protectors.

I understand that the inventor made a fortune out of it, since he had a monopoly of the business. But that does not matter now, for he died some years later, leaving all his money behind him, and the people got their shoes and have been wearing them ever since.

The moral of this apologue is that governmental interference, however arbitrary, and individual initiative, however mercenary, may sometimes work together for the good of all. If shoes did not get their start this way, various other things did, and at any rate the story illustrates the way allied science softens the asperities of the earth and protects humanity from injury. Man is a featherless, furless, hoofless biped, exposed to all weathers and wounds. Yet he has managed to make himself fairly comfortable in all climates and feared by the most formidable of beasts. Climate is forever beyond his control, yet the caveman of the Mediterranean was, by the invention of fire, enabled to follow the edge of the ice-sheet as it retreated at the end of the glacial epoch and inhabit the northern region. Man makes a local climate in his home or factory, as warm or cool, as dry or humid, as he likes, wherever he may live.

The alternation of night and day are unalterable, yet man has rearranged the periods of light and dark to suit his duties or accommodate his pleasures. From the beginning man had the power to make it night whenever he wished by simply shutting his eyes, but he has only recently acquired the art of making it day when he wants to by simply pressing a white button.

Born devoid of protective integument, man has made for himself artificial skins which he can change with fashion and adjust to the weather, so that he need not pant like a polar bear in the tropics or shiver like a monkey in the arctics.

He can outsoar the eagle on his self-made wings. He can outrun the deer in his automobile. He can dive longer than the whale in his submarine. He can lift an elephant in air with his engines.

But man is only beginning to make himself at home on this planet. He is not yet awake to his power and possibilities. He is lacking in a thousand things as necessary to his comfort as shoes and does not yet know that he lacks them. We are still living in the barefoot age for the most part, hardening our soles by bruises and cuts, which we might avoid if we knew a little more and used what little we do know.

31

SUMMER DRINKS

The chief means we have of keeping cool in hot weather is by evaporation, and evaporation requires a constant supply of water. But plain water soon palls. Man craves variety and ever strives to turn his necessities into pleasures. So to avoid tepidity and monotony he takes his liquid hot or cold and adds flavors and pungencies of all sorts.

It is in America, where the summers are hot and dry and the people temperate and ingenious, that the art of mixing beverages cold and soft has reached its height. The American soda-fountain has transformed the drug-store, which used to be as unattractive as a dentist's room and so sought only by the sick, into the palace of delight, the haunt of the healthy.

The walls and mirrors back of a soda-fountain are filled with the names of new drinks, or the new names of drinks, and still the patrons call for original combinations. But in spite of the variety in appearance and taste the composition of the summer beverages can be easily comprehended when we classify their ingredients according to their purpose instead of their origin. If we attempt such a classification we find that the qualities in demand are sourness, sweetness, flavor, effervescence, color, and stimulation. Representatives of most or all of these groups are to be found in any of the popular drinks, but their sources are various.

For the sourness we have a choice of many organic acids, chiefly the citric of the lemon, the tartaric of

the grape, the acetic of vinegar, and the lactic of milk.
The inorganic acids are not used, as they are too strong
and not assimilable, with the possible exception of phosphoric. Acid sodium phosphate has been found by
experiments on German soldiers to be stimulant and
energizer. But you don't get much phosphoric acid
in the ordinary phosphate drink.

For sweetness we have the sugars of many kinds, but
the most important are sucrose (cane-sugar), glucose
and fructose, which occur in all ripe fruits. Sugar
is better than alcohol as a "self-starter" and can be
guaranteed not to intoxicate the weakest brain.

The flavors are, chemically speaking, mostly the
esters or ethereal salts of alcohols and fatty or aromatic
acids. These give the savor and perfume of all the
fruits and flowers, and from these we extract them,
although as soon as the chemist finds out what they
are he can make them in the laboratory.

For effervescence, the old reliable carbon dioxide
is universally used for the non-alcoholic as it is for
the alcoholic beverages. Carbon dioxide is a weak and
volatile acid, serving to stimulate the palate and stomach and quickly passing off. It is this gas that gives
the effervescence to all mineral waters, and if one does
not want to clog his system with a lot of salts such as
happen to occur in some European *bain* or *bad*, he can
take "plain soda," which does not contain any soda but
is merely distilled or tap water charged with carbon
dioxide.

An attractive color is itself an appetizer and excites
the flow of the digestive secretions. The red circus
lemonade of our childhood's days was the first crude

attempt at enhancing the charms of nature in the way of tinting beverages. Now we can satisfy all tastes, whether quiet or loud, since the dispenser has at his command a palatable palette that includes not only all the colors found in the fruit, flower, and leaf but any number of harmless aniline dyes beside.

Those who eschew alcohol but still demand some stimulant usually make use of caffein, which is the essential principle of tea and coffee and is now used in certain popular summer drinks. Caffein is also contained in cassina and yerba-mate, which the Department of Agriculture suggests as beverage material. The still milder alkaloid of cocoa, theobromine, does not seem to have been yet employed in this way. In these prohibition days aromatic ammonia is coming into use as a substitute for the banished—or outlawed—alcohol. Both caffein and ammonia are pure stimulants and are not followed by the depressant reaction of alcohol; and you can't get drunk on them if you try.

It is with the unconscious aim of getting in some or all of these six kinds of ingredients that human ingenuity has developed the art of mixing summer drinks. An old-fashioned refreshment of the harvest field was switchel, wherein the sourness was given by vinegar, the flavor and pungency by ginger and the sweetness by molasses or maple-sugar. We are also indebted to our grandfathers or grandmothers for the discovery of root or birch beer. The aromatics for this were mostly obtained by gathering such roots, barks, leaves, and seeds as grew in the neighborhood and had been discovered—doubtless by those enterprising experimenters, the children—to be tasty and non-poisonous.

With the aid of sugar, hops, and yeast, the necessary carbonic acid was developed, together with a trace— or more—of alcohol.

That old favorite, iced tea, is appearing in new forms of late by adding to its caffein other popular ingredients. When a slice of lemon was dropped in it became *à la russe*, but what to call it now with strawberry, raspberry, or pineapple in it would puzzle a French culinary dictionary. Fruit punches also have become indescribably complicated since the fruits of all lands and all seasons are at our disposal. Hawaii is sending us canned pineapple juice, which is said to have digestive powers, and anyhow makes a palatable drink alone or is an agreeable addition to any other. The lemon we have long known, but the lime is not yet so familiar as it is in England, where it is used for the prevention of scurvy in the British navy and merchant marine and has given the nickname of "lime-juicers" to the sailors. This prophylactic effect is due to the Vitamin C that all the citrus fruits contain. Tomatoes have more vitamins, and I wonder why nobody has made a fountain drink out of tomato-juice. Nothing is more refreshing, when one is on a long hot camping trip, than to knock two holes in the top of a can of tomatoes with a hatchet and drink out of one of them. Grape-juice and orange-juice are rapidly growing in popularity. Our paternal Government has introduced us to a new summer drink, that is, grape-fruit juice, which, according to instructions sent out by the Department of Agriculture, can be easily preserved, provided it can be boiled out of contact with iron and bottled out of contact with air.

Ginger-ale, deservedly one of the most popular of summer drinks, may be regarded as a descendant of the farm switchel with the substitution of citric in the place of acetic acid—doubtless an improvement—and the addition of such aromatics as the taste and generosity of the manufacturer allow. The dry ginger-ale, recently introduced from England, is likely to contain more capsicum than ginger, but perhaps is none the worse for that. Sarsaparilla also has changed its nature without changing its name, for wintergreen and sassafras have more or less completely usurped the place of the title rôle. This, however, is no great loss, since sarsaparilla no longer keeps in medical circles its former reputation as a blood purifier.

On the whole, then, we have reason to be proud of the progress that has been made in the production of summer drinks. Ingredients actually harmful or even deleterious have been mostly eliminated. The chief danger that besets the habitués of the soda-fountain is lack of cleanliness on the part of the dispenser, especially in the rinsing of the glasses. With due regard for this and for the temperature and condition of his stomach, the thirsty one may face the fountain without fear and pick out from the fancy names upon the mirror whatever seems most enticing at the time.

32

THE SUN-CURE

Old Tut-ankh-Amen, who figured so prominently in our daily press, was brought up as a unitarian sun-worshiper but later relapsed into the priestly polytheism, which was a pity, for if a people must pick its god from natural objects, as the Egyptians in their blindness had to, it is better to take the sun than to adore cats, crocodiles, hippopotamuses, and beetles. The sun is quite literally the source of our vital and mechanical energy, the sole support of all life and motion on the earth, as the ancient Egyptian hymn declares, and we are beginning to recognize, perhaps I should say rerecognize, that it may cure diseases, too.

For man has a poor memory. He forgets much that previous generations have learned. The Romans used to make great use of the sun for the healing of sores and the maintenance of health. Pliny, in writing about how his aged friend, Spurinna, kept his youthful vigor, says:

When the baths are ready, which in winter is about three o'clock and in summer about two, he undresses himself, and if there happens to be no wind, he walks about in the sun. After this he puts himself into prolonged and violent motion at playing ball; and by this sort of exercise he combats the effect of old age.

But we northern races, having to wear thick clothing and stay in warm houses, got out of the habit of exposing our skins to sunshine. The invention of windowglass led us astray, for glass lets through all the light that we can see, and we did not realize that it is opaque to the invisible ultra-violet rays, which have the strongest effect upon the skin for good or ill. We thought if we had fresh air and sunlight (even though strained through glass) we had all that we needed from nature.

The rediscovery of the curative power of direct sun-shine came by accident. In a hospital for rickety children it was found that the child who had the luck to lie in a certain cot exposed to the rays of the sun recovered with amazing rapidity.

Experiments on white rats gave the clue to the secret. They developed rickets even in the sunlight, if kept in a glass box, but not if they received occasionally the direct rays of the sun. The mercury-vapor lamp—that bluish tube that makes you look so ghostly at the photographer's—worked as well as the sun, provided that the inclosing tube was made of quartz instead of glass.

This indicates that the curative rays are mainly those with the very short wave-length that lie beyond the violet end of the spectrum, for these rays cannot pass through glass although they will through quartz. The X-rays, which have the power to penetrate to the depths of the body and break up the flesh, causing sores, if left on too long, lie far beyond these in the spectrum of radiation. Sunlight does not contain X-rays; other-wise we should not be able to carry our photographic plate-holders into the open.

In 1917 Dr. A. F. Hess of New York in studying the seasonal variation of disease observed that rickets was most common in February when sunshine is weak-est and briefest, and that it decreased to almost nothing in the summer. He has found that rickets in infants could be prevented and cured by exposure to the sun's rays for half an hour a day.

The babies in the hospital behind glass windows de-veloped rickets, while those set outside in the sun did not, although both were fed on the best of milk. When the rickety infants were put out on the porch in the sun their bones stiffened up and their blood showed an increase of the phosphates necessary for bone building.

It seems that the sunshine has much the same effect as an addition to the diet of a vitamin which is contained in certain fats and promotes growth. So rickets can be cured by either a dose of cod-liver oil or sunshine. There is no question which remedy the children will take if they have their choice.

Since 1903 Dr. Rollier has been successfully treating tuberculous sores and swellings by exposing them to sunshine on his Alpine farm at Leysin, Switzerland, where the boys work and play all day long in the open with no clothing but a breech-clout. The British have taken up the sun-cure although they have not much of any sunshine to work with. The Germans have carried their *Nacktkultur* as they have their other forms of *Kultur* beyond the limits allowable in other countries. If sun-bathing becomes a fad it will put the police into the delicate position of having to determine how far a coat of tan is a proper substitute for other clothing.

What the action of the ultra-violet rays is on the human system is not yet known. The sunlight falling on the skin somehow changes the composition of the blood and may cause it to resist the poisons, and possibly kill the germs, that cause disease. Sunning is said to alleviate rheumatism and to hasten the recovery of convalescents from fevers and wounds. The "blue glass" fad that some of us are old enough to remember may have been on the right track—if the glass had only been left out.

Where the patient is too weak to sit up, the treatment is begun with two-minute doses several times a day and increased by two minutes daily for a fortnight, with protection for the eyes and head. It is necessary to avoid both chill and sunburn. Thin white cotton cloth does not seriously shut out the curative rays.

When the greater part of the naked body is exposed to the direct rays of the sun, blood-pressure falls and respiration diminishes in rate but increases in depth, so that the volume of air inhaled is greater. Sunshine striking the skin expands the capillaries and brings more blood to the surface. The number of white and red corpuscles increases, and these promote the healing process. The best results are obtained when the skin is exposed to the unfiltered radiation from the sun and yet kept from overheating by a light breeze or bodily movement. In our winter rooms we get the reverse of this, overheating and no radiation.

33

The Science of Keeping Cool

The problem of hot weather is not, as some folks seem to think, how to keep the heat out.

It is how to get the heat out.

The body temperature sticks pretty close to the normal point of 98.6 degrees Fahrenheit, and unless the air temperature gets above that we do not take on heat from the air.

For heat, like water, runs downhill. It passes from a higher to a lower temperature. The steeper the grade the faster the flow. That's where the difficulty comes in. For we have to keep our internal temperature at the normal point, whatever it may be outside, and there are only a thin skin and some clothes between. When the weather is cold we have no trouble in getting rid of the heat we produce from the food we eat, for it runs off rapidly, so rapidly that we have to put on more clothes to check it. But as the air temperature rises nearer to that of our own the current of escaping heat slows up and finally sets back if the temperature goes over 99.

We shut down the furnace in our houses when winter goes. But we cannot shut down the furnace inside of us, because the works would stop. Our internal furnace serves as a power-house as well as a heater. We have to keep the engine going night and day, and that requires a certain amount of fuel, though of course we do not need so much in summer-time as when we have the heating-plant on too.

A man who is not doing much, "just up and about," will have to have 2400 calories of food a day. If he is working, he will need 500 or 1000 more. So even if he lives in idleness he has to get rid of heat at the rate of 100 calories an hour on the average, which is about as much heat as is given off by four ordinary electric lights.

Now, this heat can be got rid of in two ways: it can run away or be carried away.

It will run away if the temperature of the surrounding air is enough lower than the body and there is not too much cloth between.

It can be carried away by water. Water can carry

more heat without showing it than anything else in the world. A quart of water will take on a calory of heat and only show a rise of less than two degrees Fahrenheit. When a quart of water evaporates it carries off about 500 calories. If, then, you sweat a quart this is the quantity of heat you are getting rid of, provided the perspiration evaporates from the skin. Here is the difficulty. If the air holds already all the water it can take up, then you cannot get the benefit of the absorption of heat through evaporation. So when the air is saturated with moisture, or, as the weather man puts it, when the humidity is 100, then you say "this is muggy weather," and you complain that the heat is intolerable even though the thermometer does not stand high.

Your own internal thermometer, your sense of temperature, only registers loss and gain. You feel warm when you are gaining heat. You feel cool when you are losing heat. You can lose heat by radiation only when the air is cooler than your skin. You can lose heat by evaporation only when the air is drier than your skin.

Remember, it is only the layer next to your skin that counts. If the air there has a temperature of 99 degrees and a humidity of 100 per cent, then you cannot get cool either way. In that case you must drive away the layer of hot moist air and let some that is drier and cooler get at your skin, which you can do by means of a breeze, or, in default of that a fan.

34

Women As Chemists

In days of old when men were bold and wives their humble servitors, most of the chemical industries were in the hands of women. Cooking, cleaning, dyeing, tanning, pharmacy, and ceramics—these were mostly women's work among primitive peoples. But when it was found that these household industries could be carried on in large establishments with more profit and less labor, the men as usual took them one by one away from the women. The question then arose whether women should follow their lost occupation from the family to the factory, or be content with such dull and ill paid branches of these industries as were left to her in the home. This is a question that may be settled by the party most concerned, for man has had such a hard time in the past finding out what is woman's place and keeping her in it that he has about given up the job and is ready to say, ''Go and try it for yourself if you like.''

It is been found that a far-seeing Providence has furnished the feminine brain with all the necessary neurons for the comprehension of even the most complicated of chemical formulæ and that feminine fingers have sufficient delicacy of touch to manipulate the most fragile of chemical apparatus. All our universities except the more moss-covered ones now provide instruction for women on equal terms with men.

Women have had to pry open some of the professions by disguising themselves as men. ''George Sand'' and

"George Eliot" gained a hearing which they could not under their own names. I once overheard a professor of chemistry in a great university say to one of his feminine Ph.D.'s, who was writing an application for a position, "Perhaps it would be sufficient to use only your initials in signing your name." There still lingers some prejudice against women chemists in industry and even in schools, but here as elsewhere "there is always room at the top." Any woman who shows a genius for original research can find opportunity.

Men in chemistry have not from the first been so ungenerous toward the other sex as men in many other fields. Listen to the gallant if somewhat patronizing language with which Thomas P. Smith extends a welcome to his fair colleagues in the Annual Oration that he delivered before the Chemical Society of Philadelphia on April 11, 1798:

I shall now present you with the last and most pleasing revolution that has occurred in chemistry. Hitherto we have beheld this science entirely in the hands of *men;* we are now about to behold *women* assert their just, though too long neglected claims, of being participators in the pleasures arising from a knowledge of chemistry. . . . What may we not expect from such an accession of talents? How swiftly will the horizon of knowledge recede before our united labours! And what unbounded pleasure may we not anticipate in treading the paths of science with such companions?

In the same volume [1] I find a quotation from another eighteenth-century book, "Letters for Literary Ladies," that will be of interest to the twentieth-century women, and will amuse the athletic girl and the flapper:

[1] President Edgar Fays Smith's "Chemistry in America."

Chemistry is a science particularly suited to women, suited to their talents and their situation; chemistry is not a science of parade, it affords occupation and infinite variety; it demands no bodily strength, it can be pursued in retirement; it applies immediately to useful and domestic purposes; and whilst the ingenuity of the most inventive mind may be exercised, there is no danger of inflaming the imagination; the judgment is improved, the mind is intent upon realities, the knowledge that is acquired is exact, and the pleasure of the pursuit is a sufficient reward for the labour.

Nowadays our women do not think that "the pleasure of the pursuit is a sufficient reward for the labour," but demand cold cash in addition. And they are getting it—not yet perhaps equally with men for the same quality of work, but in increasingly adequate amount as they prove their ability in these new fields.

35

THE ADVANTAGE OF TAN

The Ethiopian cannot change his skin, but the white man can. That is where the white man has the advantage, for when he is exposed to the sun he gradually becomes a colored man. (The negro is not a "colored" man; he was born so.)

The white skin automatically protects itself against the injurious action of the sun's rays by developing a layer of dark pigment in the deeper part of the epidermis. That is, the brunettes and the tannable blonds have this power. The incorrigible blonds that burn and blister will have to stay in the house or take to charcoal face-powder.

Black looks black to us because it absorbs and keeps the visual rays of light. White looks white to us because it reflects them back to our eyes. White clothing is therefore better than black in the tropics because it sheds sunshine better. Black cloth absorbs about twice as much of the visible rays as white.

We might conclude from this that a white skin would be better than black in warding off sunshine. And so it would if heat were the only thing involved. But it is not. The sun's rays contain, besides the heat that we feel and the light that we can see, certain rays that we can neither feel nor see but which have a powerful effect upon the skin for good or ill. These are the rays that have a shorter wave-length than the violet, which are the shortest that can be seen. They are therefore called the "ultra-violet." Ordinary sunshine contains about ten per cent of these ultra-violet rays; more if the air is dry, less if it is damp. Of the rest of the solar radiation about fifty per cent is in the form of visible light and about forty per cent in the form of dark heat or "infra-red" rays. The heat-rays are absorbed about the same whether the skin or clothing be black or white.

But with the short-wave rays at the other end of the spectrum it is different. These are more energetic than the long-wave rays but are more easily discouraged and do not penetrate so far into the skin. If you hold up your hand and look through it toward the sun you will see that the light that gets through the thin parts of the fingers looks red. That means the long red waves, and of course the longer heat-waves, go through, while the short violet waves, and of course the shorter ultra-violet, are caught and held in the flesh and blood.

This is fortunate, for the ultra-violet rays are fatal to the living cells of the body. The X-rays that have waves ten thousand times shorter than the violet rays are so powerful that they are used to burn away cancers. The visible rays of short wave-length are still strong enough to cause sunburn.

What we need, then, in the skin is some sort of a contrivance that will take these short light and ultra-light waves and transform them to the harmless heat-waves, what the electricians call a "step-down transformer."

Well, we have such a contrivance in tan. First the thin horny outside layer of the skin catches and converts to heat the ultra-violet. Then the short-wave visible rays, violet and blue, are caught by the pigmented cells lying beneath. The longer waves, the yellow, red, and infra-red, penetrate further but do no harm except to make us warmer. A thin-skinned person well tanned is better off than a thick-skinned person, because the former is sufficiently protected against the lethal rays and yet can get rid of his own internal heat more readily by radiation through his thin skin.

The tan serves another purpose than mere protection. For the nerve-endings lie between the pigment cells, and when they are excited by the heat from the transformed light they dilate the vessels in the skin and so send out the sweat which by evaporation cools off the body.

It is not necessary to carry the pigmentation to an extreme as the negro does. A good browning will in-

sure against the injurious and secure the beneficial
effects of sunning. The children of negroes and dark-
skinned Italians are more likely to have rickets than
white children. So it seems that here as elsewhere
the golden mean is safest.

36

FROM COMPLEXES TO GLANDS

How swiftly the spot-light of popular interest shifts
from one part of the stage to another! The eyes of dis-
tressed humanity turn eagerly toward any quarter
that appears to promise health and happiness.

A few years ago psychoanalysis was all the rage.
Now endocrinology is coming into fashion. Those who
recently were reading Freud and Jung have now taken
up with Berman and Harrow. Those who formerly
were rushing to have complexes extracted are now anxious to have glands implanted. Away with psychology!
Rah for physiology! Anything hailing from Vienna is
bound to boom.

As fads there is not much to choose between them.
Popular expectations always run far ahead of the
march of sober science, which must make sure of every
step as it goes. Both these have a certain foundation
of fact and promise much for the future, though neither
can fulfil the anticipations of the public at present.

But the scientific basis of the glandular idea is much
more solid and substantial. An emotional complex is
after all a figment of the imagination, but when you

get out a chemical compound, extracted, purified and identified, you have hold of something tangible, and when you put it back into the patient you can regulate the dose and record the reaction.

The psychoanalyst may be able, as he boasts, to "pluck from the memory a rooted sorrow," but another will grow in its place so long as the soil remains the same. The morbid idea once eradicated reappears, transformed or transferred, as often as it is ousted. None of us can avoid shocking experiences, disturbing thoughts, and repressed desires, but they need not annoy us persistently unless the chemistry of the body is out of kilter. Any splinter or scratch will fester if the bodily system is unsound, but severe wounds will soon heal if the composition of the blood is all right. There are microbes everywhere, but we do not catch all the diseases we can. It is the same with mental microbes. A psychoanalyst may interpret your dreams as he likes best, but a doctor can give you any kind of dream you want by a dose of hashish, strychnine, or opium, or you can get dreams that you don't want by an untimely mince-pie or an unruly Welsh rabbit.

Physiologists now lay many bodily disorders, as capitalists do industrial disorders, to the pernicious activity of "agitators." The physiologist, since he prefers to talk Greek, calls them "hormones," but the word means the same. At least a half-dozen of these hormones are already known. They are marketed among the four hundred by-products of our packing-houses. Two of them, thyroxin and adrenalin, are definite chemical compounds and can be made synthetically. Soon the chemist will capture them all, and possibly he may make stronger and better ones than the glands turn out in their old-fashioned way. There may be giants on the earth in those days, such as Wells foretold in "The Food of the Gods."

These hormones determine our temper and our temperament. They decide whether we shall be tall or short, thick or thin, stupid or clever. They mold our features and control our characters. A minute amount of certain secretions will make one more masculine or feminine, older or younger.

But until the chemist can manufacture them in the laboratory and we can carry them in a vest-pocket case we are dependent upon more or less active and impure extracts from the glands to supply our functional deficiencies. Or—and this is the latest sensation of the hour—we may be grafted with a gland from some animal. Unfortunately, the glands of the lower animals do not set well in the human system. Those of the apes work best, which goes to prove that they are blood relations of ours, Mr. Bryan to the contrary notwithstanding. In any case the relief is not likely to last long, for the borrowed gland may succumb to the same influences that invalidated the natural organ.

In spite of the startling experiments of Voronov and Steinach on the rejuvenation of rats and sheep, science is not yet in a position to meet the old demand for an elixir of life. Dr. Brown-Séquard of Paris, who thought thirty years ago that he had found something of the sort in an extract of goat glands, did not live long enough to demonstrate his discovery. The rich old man who went to Vienna to regain his youth and came to London to prove the success of Steinach's operation died on the eve of his lecture on "How I Was Made Twenty Years Younger."

But there will be plenty of people eager to try the new methods, urged by the same motive that drove Ponce de Léon to seek the fountain of immortal youth in the vicinity of Palm Beach.

37

GEOLOGISTS GET AN EXTENSION OF TIME

There was a deadlock between the astronomers and geologists at the beginning of this century. The geologists, having been converted to evolution by Darwin, needed lots of time for the development of the varied forms of life by the gradual process of natural selection, the only process they knew. Then, too, they figured out that it must have taken at least 300,000,000 years to lay the sedimentary rocks and to make the ocean as salty as it is. Man, who is one of the latest settlers on this planet, seems to have been here more than 250,000 years, and the earliest fossils are buried so deep that animal life must have existed some 60,000,000 years at the lowest estimate.

But here the astronomers and physicists interposed a veto on the geologists and paleontologists. "You can't have anything like such a length of time," they said, "for the earth was a molten mass long after the time when you say life began, and was a fiery gas-ball long after you talk of oceans. The earth is the offspring of the sun, and the sun itself is only 20,000,000 years old."

This time limit was the estimate of Lord Kelvin, based upon the idea that the sun's heat came from its contraction by gravitation, for no other source of its heat was surmised at that time. He figured out that if all the particles of matter that make up the sun had fallen together from an infinite distance the heat produced by their impact would not be more than enough to keep the sun radiating at its present rate for more than twenty million years.

If, however, somebody should discover another and more abundant source of heat than the shrinkage of the sun, then, of course, the astronomers would be willing to grant the geologists an extension of time for the building up of the world and its inhabitants.

Well, somebody did discover an unknown source of heat abundant enough to satisfy the most extreme demands of the astronomers. This was Madame Curie with her radium, a metal that is continually giving off heat from a secret store within its atom. It appeared then that some of the heavy elements in breaking down into lighter ones, as radium breaks down into lead and helium, give off large amounts of heat for thousands of years. It was later found that atoms of a light element might combine together to form a heavier element and likewise give off heat in immense quantities. For instance, if a pound of hydrogen were to condense to form helium the resulting helium would weigh a little less than a pound, but there would be given off as much heat as would be produced by the burning of 10,000 tons of coal.

Unfortunately no way is known of working this

process so that it will help us out in the winter's coal
shortage, but it has helped the astronomers and geologists out of their dilemma. For the astronomers, having
now a source of heat sufficient to keep the sun and stars
going for as long as even they can imagine, can afford
to be generous with the geologists in the matter of time.
Professor Eddington of Cambridge made this conces-
sion handsomely when he said recently:

Lord Kelvin's estimate of the extent of geological time need
not now be taken any more seriously than Archbishop Ussher's
and the geologist may claim anything up to 10,000 million
years without provoking a murmur from astronomers.

This liberal allowance ought to satisfy the geologists,
especially since they have learned from Mendel that
evolution may proceed by jumps instead of by the slow
accumulation of minute variations which Darwin had
in mind.

38

How Old Is Disease?

There is a curious belief still lingering in the popular
mind that diseases came in with civilization, that primitive men and animals lived in a state of perpetual health
and died a natural death; though it is hard to see what
is meant by "natural" in this sense. Even Mrs. Char-
lotte Perkins Gilman, who is very much of a modernist,
falls into this folk fallacy, for in her poem on "The Little Eohippus" she makes the caveman prophesy:

We are going to wear great piles of stuff
Outside our proper skins!
We are going to have diseases!
And accomplishments!! and sins!!!

"It was a clinching argument to the Neolithic mind," but really it was not so. The Neolithic man was all too familiar with diseases and doubtless had also his accomplishments and sins. He suffered from rheumatism and "cave gout" and toothache, for caverns are damp and chilly lodgings. He shared the diseases as he did the lodgings of the cave-bear and saber-toothed cats. The earliest human bones, if indeed they can be called human—those of the ape-man who lived in Java some half million years ago—bear the marks of a painful malady. The skull of the Dawn Man of Piltdown, England, a hundred thousand years old, is deformed by disease.

The men of the Stone Age must have suffered frightfully from headache, for they allowed the tribal doctor to cut holes in their skulls with flint knives to let out the demon that was causing the pain. And if the patient was not cured or killed by this treatment he sometimes tried it again when he had another headache. Dr. Roy L. Moodie of the University of Chicago, in his new book, "The Antiquity of Disease," says: "A few ancient skulls reveal five cruel operations, which had all healed. The patient has survived them all." But he suggests that since this custom of trepanning was practised most commonly in Peru the patient may have had the relief of a local anesthetic in the form of a few leaves of coca, the plant that gives us cocaine.

But eons before the human era the dumb animals had

to endure all manner of diseases. The dinosaurs of the Mesozoic era had "misery in the bones"—and such bones as they were! You have seen them in the museum. It must have been worse than a giraffe's sore throat. "Pott's disease" was doing its wicked work millions of years before Dr. Pott was born, though this sounds like an anachronism. This is shown by the discovery of backbones of saurians that had been stiffened by tuberculosis. Tumors are to be seen on reptile skeletons buried in the rock chalk of Kansas, and broken bones showing signs of bacterial infection have been found as far back as the Permian of Texas.

Geologists have to depend mostly upon bones for their knowledge of ancient diseases, since the softer parts do not leave fossil remains; but the stems of crinoids in the coal-fields are found bored into by worms, and it is apparent that the mollusks, crustaceans, and plants of earlier ages were afflicted with parasites and other pests.

The earliest and simplest forms of plant and animal life, the bacteria and protozoa, seem envious of later arrivals and wage perpetual war on them to this day. The larger animals prey upon the smaller, but so do the smaller upon the larger, and the most dangerous of beasts of prey are the littlest. When man appeared on the planet he found the microbe lying in wait for him. Sooner or later, we all fall victims to the lower forms of life, and, after death if not before, become the food of our invisible enemies. Even Tut-ankh-Amen, embalmed and entombed for the perpetual preservation of his personality, will ultimately be gathered into the recurrent cycles of common life.

39

Has Science Reached Its Limit?

"What is there left for me to discover?" is the common thought of the student as he looks about the library with shelves packed with books or the museum with cases filled with neatly labeled specimens. He realizes that when he enters upon research he is competing not only with his contemporaries but with all his predecessors. No tariff can protect him from the pauper labor of antiquity.

"What are you scientists going to do when you find out everything about everything?" is a common remark of visitors to a laboratory. The scientist will doubtless reply that life is not long enough to find out everything about anything, but even he is likely to harbor the delusion that all the really big things have now been discovered and that future investigators will find pretty poor picking. Some scientists have been so rash as to put this opinion into print, much to the amusement of later generations. For instance, the great French mineralogist, Hauy, wrote at the beginning of the nineteenth century:

Electricity, enriched by the labor of so many distinguished physicists, seems to have reached a time when a science has no more important steps before it and only leaves to those who cultivate it the hope of confirming the discoveries of their predecessors and of casting a brighter light on the truths revealed.

But we count this the beginning of our knowledge of electricity rather than its end, for over in London at this very time young Michael Faraday in his basement room at the Royal Institution was working out the relationship between electricity and magnetism which has led to the dynamo and the radio.

One might think that such a blunder as this would have made later scientists cautious about thinking that nothing much remained to discover, but no, for we find in 1894 the catalogue of one of the largest universities in the United States publishing at the head of its list of courses in physics the following discouraging statement:

> While it is never safe to affirm that the future of physical science has no marvels in store . . . it seems probable that most of the grand underlying principles have been firmly established and that further advances are to be sought chiefly in the rigorous application of these principles to all the phenomena which come under our notice. . . . An eminent scientist has remarked that the future truths of physical science are to be looked for in the sixth place of decimals.

But the very next year Röntgen discovered the X-rays that led to radium and the electron.

When Newton laid down the law of gravitation the solar system was reduced to a simple mechanism and the movements of the planets could be accurately predicted. What was there left for the astronomer to do? Bigger telescopes would doubtless reveal more satellites and show finer markings on the moon, but how could we ever hope to learn anything about the composition of the heavenly bodies? Yet now we can know how the electrons behave inside the atoms of stars whose light requires thousands of years to reach us, and Einstein has pointed out that even Newton's law requires modification.

Some branches of science may well have reached a terminal. I suppose it is safe to say that about all the large animals on the earth have been discovered and described. It is true that the okapi, which is almost as conspicuous as a giraffe, managed to keep himself concealed in the African jungle until 1900, but not many such can have escaped the eye of the zoölogist. But he can make no end of queer looking animals when zoölogy becomes a constructive instead of a descriptive science.

The scientific discoveries of the twentieth century have not only been more numerous than in any previous century but they have been greater. Our investigators are not engaged in verifying the sixth decimal but are projecting far-reaching and fundamental theories.

When you throw wood on a camp-fire in the night you expand the lighted area, but you also extend the circle of the surrounding darkness.

40

How the Other Half of the Plant Lives

How pleasant and peaceful looks a field of growing grain! Its stalks standing in neat rank and file, spaced apart like soldiers in a setting-up exercise, idly waving their green banners in the breeze. A fresh supply of carbon dioxide comes to them with every breeze, and all they have to do is to open their stomata and breathe it in. No shortage. No competition. Nothing to worry about. Happy plants!

But call no being happy till you know the whole of

THE OAT PLANT, VISIBLE
AND INVISIBLE

From "Development and
Activities of Roots of Crops."
(Carnegie Institution.)

its life. Look beneath the soil and you will see a different and uglier aspect. Here the struggle for existence is fierce and unceasing. The roots reach out in all directions in search of water and food. Those pretty flaunting leaves above are lavish in their waste of water, and this all has to be procured by the humble hidden rootlets and pumped up to the top. The flowers and fruits are dainty in their tastes and insist upon certain salts that are hard to find in the soil.

So upon the tiny tender rootlets devolves the task of forcing their way through the stubborn subsoil in competition with their own kind and foreign weeds. If a well watered spot or a bed of nitrates is struck there is a rush of all the roots of the neighborhood in that direction. A drawing of the root systems of a path of growing plants looks like the map of competing railroad companies in territory just opened for settlement.

A band of investigators under Professor John E. Weaver, who is associated with the œcological work of Dr. Clements carried on under the auspices of the Carnegie Institution of Washington, have been for many years studying the life history of root development in the chief crops of Nebraska, Kansas, and Colorado, and they have reached some remarkable results that seem likely to alter methods of agriculture. They find, for instance, that the cereals go deeper for their nourishment than has been commonly supposed. At Peru, Nebraska, the roots of wheat and oats reach depths of six and eight feet. That is, the roots of the grain go more than twice as deep into the ground as the stalks stand above it. Corn rises to a stately and imposing height. Yet corn sticks down as far as it sticks up. A single corn-stalk may have some forty feeders in the ground, and gather water and nutrients from four feet all around and from eight feet below. All the cereals have two sets of roots, one running out laterally and the other striking straight down.

The potato pursues different tactics. All its roots start out sideways first, and then when they get out a foot or two they turn and run down.

The old idea that a crop got most of its nutrition from the surface layer of six to eight inches and that the condition of the subsoil did not matter much is exploded by these investigations. For it is found that winter wheat and rye in the prairie States get the greatest amount of their food and drink from below three feet and some of it from the five-foot level.

But here is a funny thing. If the young roots, as they are starting out in life, happen to strike a spot rich in nitrates or phosphates, they are likely to linger there too long in working the claim, so that the root system never reaches a full and sufficient development. In just the same way many a young man's ambition has been dulled by paying him too high a salary on the start. The lesson is to put the fertilizer a little out of reach of the roots and make 'em scramble for it.

Another practical suggestion arising out of this research is that two crops can be grown on the same ground alternately or even at the same time. For, if one crop has short thick roots and the other long spreading roots they will not interfere, but rather help each other. They will feed from different levels.

We may then come to see two-storied agriculture in the semi-arid region, perhaps even subterranean skyscrapers—so to speak.

41

PERCENTAGE ALIVENESS

When I dropped into Professor Winthrop J. V. Osterhout's laboratory at Woods Hole by the sea I found him at first quite too busy to talk to me. Every minute or two his assistant would hand him a porcelain dish containing a few drops of cell-sap, which he would hastily analyze by counting the number of drops from a pipette that would change its color. It was a familiar chemical test, and in fact I would have thought myself in the laboratory of a chemist instead of a botanist if it had not been for some basins of dank seaweed lying around. There was a lot of electrical apparatus, too—galvanometers, resistance-boxes, and the like, such as no botanist ever bothered with in the days when I was young.

In those days the boundaries between the sciences were well defined, and a professor knew what he was professor of. Even if he taught two or more sciences, he was careful not to mix them. A botanist did not have any use for a chemist unless he wanted to borrow paraffin or alcohol from him. Now the botanists and zoölogists seem to be going over in a body to chemistry and physics. And it is a question how much will be left of the biological sciences when the physical sciences get what they want out of them.

The differences between the old botany and the new became still more apparent to me when Professor Osterhout explained to me what he was doing and what he was aiming at.

He was endeavoring to apply quantitative measurement to the processes of life, to find mathematical formulas that would show just how much a plant or animal cell is alive or how near it is to the zero point, which we call death. Mathematics is another thing that the old-fashioned botanist had no use for. It is as easy to count the petals on a flower as to count one's fingers. But Professor Osterhout's book on "Injury, Recovery and Death" is chock-full of mathematical symbols of the toughest sort.

He finds one of the best ways to measure vitality is to determine how well a cell conducts electricity. For the protoplasm that fills all cells offers considerable resistance to the passage of a current so long as it is alive, but as soon as it is dead its resistance falls off. If it is partly dead its resistance is measurably reduced.

Give Professor Osterhout various samples of seaweed of which some are thriving and others have been injured in varying degrees by putting them into water that is too fresh or too salty, or by exposure to hot sunshine or by poisoning with nicotine. They all look equally green and healthy, but by testing the conductivity he can tell you which have been injured the most and how much.

What is more, he can tell which have been injured beyond recovery and which will be restored to a state of normalcy on being put back into ordinary sea-water. If, for instance, a strip of eel-grass has been injured to the extent of five per cent by over-salting, it will recover fully when it gets back into its native element. But if it has been injured twenty-five per cent its electrical resistance rises to only ninety per cent of the normal. If the injury amounts to ninety per cent there is no recovery.

He finds whatever alters the electrical conductivity of plant or animal tissue, whether it be a crushing blow, too much heat, lack of air, lack of water, presence of poisons, or anything else, will shorten or impair the life of the organism. He comes to the conclusion that life is a series of balanced chemical processes and that when this balance is disturbed by a change in the environment one process goes faster than another, and then the creature grows or decays, thrives or declines. Dying is therefore a normal part of living. The only danger is in its getting to going too fast.

Professor Osterhout does not say anything about the

application of his discoveries and theories to human life. So far as I know, he has not carried his experiments farther up the scale of life than frog's skin. So it will be some time before we can know whether there is any sense in our crude quantitative expressions of vitality, "I feel half dead," or, "more dead than alive," by which we mean usually that we are "dead tired."

42

MAKING SUNSHINE FATAL

Sunshine is ordinarily a fine thing and is now being systematically used in the cure of wounds, tuberculous sores, and rickets. On the other hand, an overdose of solar rays may cause sunstroke, or, in lesser exposure— as many of us found on our last summer vacation—a mighty uncomfortable case of skin-scorching.

But it has recently been discovered that the human body may be so sensitized by certain substances that even a brief exposure to ordinary sunshine is danger- ous or fatal.

The discovery came about in a curious way. A Munich chemist, Herman von Tappeiner, wanted to test the physiological effect of a certain coal-tar dye- stuff called acridine.

It is customary to begin such experiments with the littlest of living things, and, if the results prove inter- esting, to work on up the scale of animals to man. By steeping hay in water one can get millions of lively little swimming creatures to work with. Then the chemical to be tested is dropped into the water in measured amounts until they are killed off. In this way the fatal dose can be easily and accurately determined. Tappeiner set a pupil to testing the poisonousness of acridine in this way, but he got conflicting results. On one day the animalcules would all be killed by a small dose of the dye, and on another day a hundred times that amount would leave them alive and wiggling.

Finally after much futile work the reason was found. If the glass of water colored with the acridine was exposed to the light the little creatures died, but if it was kept in the dark they were unharmed by the presence of the dye even in large quantity.

This clue was followed up. Other kinds of dyes were investigated and tried on higher forms of life. A colored substance obtained from blood known as hematoporphyrin was found to be fatal to white animals in sunlight. If a little of this is injected into a white mouse he is all right so long as he lives in the dark. But as soon as he is taken into the sunshine his skin begins to itch and burn. The ears, nose, and other hairless or thinly covered parts turn red, and the mouse scratches his body and rolls upon the floor to ease the irritation. Soon he shuts his eyes and sinks into a comatose state, out of which he never wakes.

After experimenting on animals it is customary for a scientist to experiment on himself. Accordingly a German physician, Fritz Meyer-Betz, injected a shot of hematoporphyrin into his own blood. He felt no ill effects while in the shade, but when he exposed himself to sunlight he began to feel like the white mice and only saved himself by a hasty flight into the house.

Evidently, then, it is possible to sensitize a human being to sunlight as we can sensitize a photographic plate by certain dyes so that even red light will fog it.

It has long been known that certain plants would so sensitize animals that they may die from exposure to the sun's rays. White pigs that feed on buckwheat are sometimes so affected. The disease is called fagopyrism, from the Latin name of buckwheat, *Fagopyrum*. But there are other herbs that have the same effect under certain circumstances, among them paintroot, St.-John's-wort, alsike clover, and knotweed.

Cattle, pigs, and sheep may feed on these plants with impunity while living in the shade, but on coming out into the sunlight, even a week or more later, they may be affected with an eruption of the skin. If taken out of the sun they may recover in a few days, but if they remain exposed they seem to go crazy, dashing about in frenzy and perhaps finally falling dead. Dark-skinned or heavily haired animals are not affected except possibly on white or bare spots.

Since such violent symptoms can be caused by sensitizing with these substances, it may be that there are other and ordinary foods which may in the long run make stock or people supersensitive to the sun, although the immediate effects are so slight as to be unnoticeable. Possibly certain articles of diet, which are harmless to those who live in houses or in northern climates, may be the reason why the white man cannot endure the tropical sun that his colored brother sustains with impunity. If this should prove to be so, then the equatorial portions of the earth might be made habitable to the Caucasian race.

43

GASOLENE AND ALCOHOL

Before prohibition the per capita consumption of gasolene and alcoholic beverages was about the same, twenty gallons a year. Now the consumption of alcoholic beverages is theoretically reduced to zero, while the consumption of gasolene has risen to seventy-seven gallons per capita.

But we may live to see these ratios reversed and gasolene decline while alcohol rises until vastly more alcohol is manufactured. For if alcohol comes into general use for fuel purposes vastly more must be manufactured than in the days when it was thought fit to drink. Nobody takes to gasolene as a beverage except the Russians, to whom it seems mild and pleasant-flavored compared with vodka. But the two fluids come into competition for satiating the thirst of the carbureter.

Now that the law will not allow us to drink liquor, we have alcohol to burn. And so soon as men get accustomed to regard alcohol as fuel instead of as food the vexatious restrictions that have been imposed upon its manufacture and sale for the last five hundred years may be removed. When that day comes the Government will be urging people to set up home stills instead of confiscating them, and this will enable spoiled grain, unsalable fruit, sawdust, and all sorts of wasted stuff to be converted into power on the spot.

For alcohol can be made out of more different things than almost anything else in the world, as those who have experimented with home-brew have found out. Any sugary, starchy, or woody material can be converted into alcohol, directly or indirectly, and there are millions of minute plants always hanging around ready to undertake the job of conversion for a bare living.

But if we have to shift from gasolene to alcohol we shall have to hunt for the cheapest and most abundant material to make it from, and it is high time that the hunting began. The saving of waste food-stuffs would not suffice. If we used corn it would take more than a quarter of our corn crop to make enough alcohol to take the place of the gasolene now used, and we shall want to use more in the future as our desire for power increases.

Probably it will be found that the tropics will grow the largest crops of saccharine material suitable for alcoholic fermentation in a season, and if so this neglected region will assume the importance that the coal-field countries now possess. There will then be hot strife for hot territory, and the alcohol power will rule the world.

There are, of course, many other conceivable possibilities. We may distil cellulose directly instead of converting it into sugar and then fermenting it to alcohol. The chemist may get up some carbon chain or ring with all the hydrogen it can hold that will make a better fuel than anything found in nature, but he will have to have something to make it out of and that something will have to be grown. Unless we find some other source of power than combustion, we must eventually grow our fuel as we use it, for fossil fuel will not last forever. We must find a way of using the sunshine of to-day instead of that which fell upon the earth in the Carboniferous era.

44

THE FIGHT AGAINST THE POTATO

What would we do without the potato? None is so poor that he cannot afford to eat it. None is so rich that he can afford to disdain it. If all the potato plants of Europe should suddenly perish and prove irreplaceable, a large part of the population would have to starve or emigrate.

Yet the people fought the potato as though it were the plague when it was first introduced into Europe. They were used to the plague and regarded it as proper punishment for their sins, but the potato, coming from the wild west of America, was new and therefore to be feared.

Sir Francis Drake is supposed to have brought the potato to England in 1586, having perhaps taken the tubers, in the course of one of his privateering cruises, from some Spanish vessel, together with other less valuable booty, such as gold and gems. Anyhow, he is credited with it by the Germans, who erected a monument in his honor at Offenburg in 1854 and struck off a medal to the British admiral as the savior of Germany in 1916, when a big potato crop enabled them to hold out another year.

But such honors always come by slow freight. It took people a hundred years or more to learn that potatoes were good for them to eat. In the eighteenth century they fed them to their pigs and cattle, which, not having the prejudices of rational men, took to them readily. The Germans then fed their prisoners of war on potatoes, and it happened that one of them was a French chemist, Parmentier, who, having been captured in 1758, was held a prisoner in Hanover for five years and had to live largely on potatoes. One would have thought he would have acquired a distaste for them, but on the contrary when he was released he urged his countrymen to cultivate the potato as a vegetable "that in Times of Necessity can be substituted for Ordinary Food." But the French, even though starving, would not eat potatoes, until finally Parmentier persuaded the king and queen to taste some and wear a bouquet of the blossoms. The people, seeing that the king and queen were not poisoned, consented to sample them for themselves.

In 1728 an attempt was made to introduce potatoes into Scotland, but they were denounced from the pulpit on two contradictory counts, that they were not mentioned in the Bible and so not fit food for Christians, and that they were the forbidden fruit, the cause of Adam's fall. They were accused of causing leprosy and fever.

In England the effort of the Royal Society to promote the cultivation of the potato was suspected to be a conspiracy of capitalists to oppress the poor. The labor leader, William Corbett, said, "It has become of late the fashion to extol the virtues of potatoes as it has been to admire the writings of Milton and Shakespeare," and he declared the working-men ought not to be induced to live on such cattle food.

When the British army was sent to fight in Flanders —not in 1914 but a hundred years before—they acquired two shocking habits: they learned to swear terribly, and they learned to eat potatoes. The monks of Bruges had introduced potato cultivation by compelling their tenants to pay part of their dues in potatoes. The farmers, seeing that the monks throve on them, began to save out some of the crop for their own use.

In Germany our own Benjamin Thompson, having become Count Rumford in Bavaria, undertook to clean the beggars out of Munich. When he had rounded them up he had to feed them, and being a student of dietetics he decided that potato-soup was the cheapest and most nutritious food he could find. But he had to smuggle the potatoes into the kitchen secretly; otherwise he would have had a hunger strike in the poorhouse.

And so, thanks to the initiative of scientists, kings, and monks, and to the involuntary assistance of pigs, prisoners, and paupers, the world got the inestimable benefit of potatoes.

I wonder what we are fighting to-day as wrongheadedly and vainly as potatoes were fought by our forefathers.

45

OUR DOMESTIC ENEMIES

Scientific detectives have discovered that a man's foes are those of his own household, his commensals. The rats and the fleas have been caught with their deadly weapons upon them, little short sticks, like the policeman's billy, with which they strike down their victims. The bomb of the anarchist misses as often as it hits, but the bacillus of the bubonic plague kills eight times out of every ten. As is common among criminals, these two enemies of our race work together at their nefarious business; the rats carry the virus from house to house; the fleas suck it from the blood of the rats and inject it into human beings.

These two pests, carriers of the Pest, are protected by the double shield of ignorance and superstition in India, where the plague lurks perpetually and occasionally breaks out and kills a million or two a year. Even if the Hindus were convinced that the animals and insects to which they so freely extend their hospitality were midnight assassins, they would still treat them as the Arab treats the enemy who has sought shelter in his tent. In the religions of the Orient the virtues assume grotesque, distorted, and unnatural forms like their idols. For thousands of years the absurdities of extreme altruism have been held up before the people of India as ideals. Before them on the street lie their living saints, giving their bodies for food to vermin as Buddha fed himself to the famished tigress. Through his self-sacrifice to the microbes the fakir is at least hastened into the hereafter if he does not attain heaven. In his first step in the path of the Yoga the aspirant toward moral perfection vows not to kill any living being.

> Kill not—for pity's sake—and lest ye slay
> The meanest thing upon its upward way.

We cannot disprove the view that all living things are of equal value in the eyes of their Creator. It may even be argued that man was made as food for the cultivation of microbes. But whether it is true or false this cosmic sympathy is not for us. We are human beings and must view the world as human beings. It is the destiny and duty of man to fight the microbe for his life as the microbe fights man for his life. Though all living beings may be of one blood, though we may have risen from the lowest ranks of animal life, either in the Darwinian or the Vedantic sense, it is nevertheless our duty to cut all our poor relations and to turn them out of our houses.

Human beings depend chiefly for health and progress upon their success in insulating themselves from other living beings and even from each other. Ablutions, anointing with oil, changes of clothing, restriction of personal contact, avoidance of dead and decaying matter—these measures for the protection of the race against its minutest and most dangerous enemies were in ancient times enforced by the authority of religion. When ecclesiastical power became too weak and negligent to uphold them, they were taken under the protection of etiquette. A new ritualism was established and enforced, covering such things as the wearing of gloves, the use of soap and water, and the manners of the table. Finally comes sanitary science, more clear-sighted and discriminating, appealing to reason instead of demanding unconditional conformity, and showing how wise in the main, as well as how futile and absurd in some of their details, were the rites which religion and fashion unconsciously devised and arbitrarily imposed.

But the doctor, in assuming control, still needs the priest and Mrs. Grundy in the enforcement of the rules of cleanliness and dietetics. There should be something of religious zeal behind the decrees of science. We should proclaim a holy war against parasites, and enforce taboos with the rigidity of South Sea islanders. Since we are so fond of reviving old religions, let us take up Zoroastrianism, in which the killing of a mosquito is regarded as an act of worship.

We are far from acting up to our lights. The housewife wages war against vermin, but she does not realize that they are more dangerous than trolley-cars. She gets more excited at the discovery of a moth than a fly, although the former only attacks clothing, not its contents. We have drain-pipes in our walls to carry off disease, but beside them are conveniently arranged passages by which roaches can carry diseases from flat to flat, so that everybody has a fair chance to catch whatever is going. Our windows are hospitably open to the malarial mosquito and the typhoid-bearing fly. Over our clothing on the street-cars crawl unmentionable insects carrying unmentionable diseases. In the fashionable hotel and restaurant the napery and porcelain are immaculate and the waiters are scrupulous; what goes on behind the screen and in the market is another story. We have got past the days when we kept the pig in the parlor, but we still keep the dog in the parlor, which is quite as bad. On the street we see the pet dog gnawing a decaying bone and nosing the foulest spot to be found, and a moment later he is cuddled in the arms of his fair and fastidious mistress and licking her cheek. We have yet to realize that it is

the dogs which are not mad that are the more dangerous. Dogs injure more people by their kisses than their
bites.

In primitive days man had to associate with the lower
animals. He needed dogs and horses, and he very
properly made friends of them. He is now learning
how to do without them, and he should, like a snob who
has risen in the world, exclude them from his circle of
intimates. The house is not intended as a zoölogical
garden. Our cities will be truly habitable only when
they contain no life but human life. Machinery may
smash us, but it does not poison our blood, rot our
bones, and corrode our flesh. All creeping, crawling
things are unclean. All our inquiline insects and animals are our enemies.

46

Do the Papers Lie About Science?

Professors as a rule have a poor opinion of the press.
They are apt to think that editors are not merely regardless of the truth of the scientific "stories" they
print but that they publish by preference the most
absurd and sensational stuff to be found. It is a common faculty saying about newspaper science that "what
is new is not true and what is true is not new." It is
also a common complaint in pedagogical circles that the
newspapers do not pay much attention to science anyhow, and that what little they do publish is antiquated
and unreliable, and altogether unworthy the notice of
educators.

But it has occurred to two scientific men to apply the scientific test to the prevalent opinion of scientists and to see whether it is true or false. Or, rather, to find out to what extent it is true and false, for to the scientist everything is relative and must be measured.

The place where this experimental method was tried was, as we might anticipate, the experimental school of Teachers College, Columbia, called the Lincoln School, which, although a new institution, has already exploded several scholastic fallacies.

The school added another such scalp to its credit when its director, Otis W. Caldwell, in collaboration with Charles W. Finley, reported the results of their statistical study of "Biology in the Public Press," which shows that scientists, in this field at least, have less reason to complain than they thought they had. Fourteen prominent papers in as many different cities from Boston to Los Angeles were taken for a month, and all the articles dealing with biological topics were clipped and classified.

The number of biological articles found during the month was 3961 and of those only 14 are classed as "fictitious." Four of these appeared in one paper, in San Francisco. Of the others, two at least cannot be regarded as serious and deliberate attempts to deceive. One is a humorous account of a hoodoo black cat on Hallowe'en, and the other tells of a rooster who had been named Harding and taught to smoke cigarettes. But I have known very strange things to happen on Hallowe'en, even on the campus; and I have been told by a reputable scientist of a rooster that would eat cigarettes, and surely chewing tobacco is as hard as smoking it, especially when one is toothless.

Fortunately the fakes are short. There are 25,596 inches in the total, and the fictitious matter only measures 48, so that according to space one would have to read on the average 500 inches of newspaper biology before he would strike an inch of fiction. Not of course that the biologists are willing to O.K. in detail all the other 499 inches. But they say that "gross misstatements of fact were not common," and on many of the dubious points there was room for honest differences of opinion. As for its being antiquated stuff, Messrs. Finley and Caldwell affirm that "Newspapers appear to be more up-to-date in things biological than are college and high school texts in the subject"; and in conclusion they turn tables on the teachers by advising them to make use of newspaper articles in class-room instruction in order to show that biology "is meaningful to the student." The professional nature-faker is going out of fashion.

47

GIVE US SHORT NAMES

When a man makes a new invention his work is not done. He should invent a new name for it. Here he is apt to fail, for, being more of a mechanic than a philologist, he turns over the job to the Greek professor who manufactures one out of old roots. So it happens that many a handy little pocket tool is handicapped by a name that wraps three times around the tongue. But the people refuse to stand for it.

Consider what a Babel-like botch has been made of the job of naming the new art of photographing action. Rival inventors, rival word-wrights, and rival systems of Greek transliteration precipitated a war of words in which the chief belligerents were animatograph, animatoscope, biograph, bioscope, chronophotography, cinema, cinematograph, cinematoscope, cineograph, cineoscope, electrograph, electroscope, kinema, kinemacolor, kinematograph, kinematoscope, kineograph, kineoscope, kinetescope, motion-pictures, moving pictures, photoplays, tachyscope, veriscope, vitagraph, vitascope, zoötrope, zoögyrograph, zoögyroscope, and zoöpraxiscope.

But the people—they call it "the movies." It is not a good name, but it is better than some at least of those listed above.

If, instead of trying to load the new machine with a name implying that it had been invented in Athens or Rome, its godfathers had given it a respectable, convenient name of one or two syllables like "kodak," "volt," "velox," or "viscose," much of this confusion might have been saved. Think how many millions of dollars, years of time, barrels of ink, and cubic miles of hot air would have been saved if "electricity" had been named in one syllable instead of five. We might even now cut it down to "el" except that by popular vote the six syllables of "elevated railroad" have been reduced to that handy term. Even professional electricians have come down to calling it the "juice." So, too, the people have found a way to reduce "radio-telephony" to a single mouthful, "radio."

The lesson of it is that if the father of a new invention does not want to have his child called by a nickname he must give it a short and snappy name on the start.

48

THE INEFFICIENCY OF AGRICULTURE

To those superstitious people who hold that Nature is perfect in all her works it must come as a shock to learn that one of the most wonderful of all natural processes and the one on which all life depends, that is, the storing up of solar energy in the green leaf, is far more inefficient than any of man's machines. It is a poor steam-engine that cannot turn into mechanical work at least twelve per cent of the heat-energy that is fed into it in the form of coal. But a green leaf is not able to catch and hold more than one per cent of the radiant energy that falls upon it from the sun.

What solar energy is caught and held is stored up, so to speak, in the form of starchy and woody stuffs, from which the energy can be released in the form of heat when the stuff is burned. But if it is food we want from the plant instead of fuel its yield is still more limited, for we human beings with our restricted digestive apparatus cannot get nutriment out of the woody fiber as we can out of the sugar and starch. How much, then, of the solar energy that falls, say, on a wheat-field can we get out in the form of the edible grain to furnish us with muscular energy?

Dr. H. A. Spoehr of the Carmel Coastal Laboratory of the Carnegie Institution of Washington has been figuring on this and reaches some startling results. An acre of ground receives in six hours of sunshine as much heat-energy as would be produced by the combustion of 16.4 tons of coal. In a growing season of ninety days at this rate per day the total income of energy would amount to 1476 tons of coal.

Now, what is the yield, likewise calculated in terms of heat-units, derivable from coal? Taking the very large crop of fifty bushels of wheat per acre and calling it all starch, we get an energy equivalent of only less than two thirds of one ton of coal.

That is to say, the farmer has received as free bounty from heaven twenty-three hundred times as much energy as he has been able to market in the shape of food.

But don't call the farmer an inefficient fellow. He only began the cultivation of wheat in the New Stone Age, say seven thousand years ago, and see how much he has improved upon Nature in the matter of yield.

And don't blame Dame Nature. She is quite indifferent to our blame or praise, but is very ready to coöperate with us when we take the trouble to learn her ways and show how they can be improved. This chlorophyl process for the fixation of solar energy, this green leaf laboratory, was one of Nature's first inventions, made perhaps sixty million years ago, and she was so well satisfied with it that she made it the foundation-stone of all earthly life and has kept it substantially unchanged to this day.

And man is not yet able to imitate Nature in this particular process, let alone surpass her. Chemists have found it possible to make some of the simpler sugars, but only in very small amounts after long and expensive labor in the laboratory—nothing like the neat and noiseless way that any leaf can carry it out. An effort is being made to get chemists and biologists to coöperate in working out the solution of the secret of photosynthesis—which is Greek for the constructive process.

49

THE BODY-GUARD

Any one who has looked at blood through a microscope will have noticed that there are two kinds of bodies floating in the fluid. There are first rolls of little round red disks looking like checker men. They carry around in a mechanical sort of way the oxygen received from the air in the lungs. But mingled with them in the blood-stream are a few bodies of a different and more active sort. They are colorless and larger than the red corpuscles and have no definite shape, but adapt themselves to their situation, crawling through crevices in the capillaries and wandering about freely among the tissues. Instead of being limited as to legs and arms as we are, they stick out any kind of a limb anywhere they may happen to need it at the moment, like the simplest of independent animals, the amœba.

The great Russian physician, Metchnikoff, discovered that these white blood corpuscles—or leucocytes, to give them their Greek name—served a useful purpose in eating up the microbes that invade our body citadel. In case of a wound they rush to the spot in increasing numbers and pile up their bodies in the breach of the skin wall. Every leucocyte is as heroic as Arnold von Winkelried. Wherever there is infection, there these defenders may be found fighting the foe and perishing by the thousand in the attempt.

But now Dr. Carrel has found that they do much more than attack disease-germs. They also in some way stimulate the structural cells of the body to greater exertions and promote the reconstruction of damaged tissue. They aid in the healing of wounds and the rebuilding of bones. They secrete an activating substance of some sort that revives the energies of cells that have grown tired or old. In short, they act not only as a patrol force to discover and combat microbic enemies but they further see to it that the other cells do their duty. No wonder that physicians have found that an examination of the blood to determine the number and activity of the leucocytes is one of the best ways of finding out what chance a patient has of overcoming his disease.

Dr. Carrel has been able to carry on the study of such processes farther than before because he found a way of working with living cells outside the body. Over eleven years ago he picked out a tiny bit of the heart of an unhatched chicken and has kept alive cells from this on glass in a warm place ever since by feeding them with suitable nutritive substances and washing away the waste products. Now the chicken, if it had been allowed to hatch, would likely have died five years ago, but this particular bit of its heart-muscle gave rise to a strain of cells which are not only living and multiplying, but seem as young as ever, and there is no apparent reason why they should not continue on indefinitely, although the matter that composes them has changed more than two thousand times. Dr. Carrel has also found that the white cells of the blood can likewise be dealt with outside the body. They can be cultivated on mica plates like colonies of bacteria and their influence on other cells studied at will in the laboratory. This, indeed, is not so surprising as his previous cultivation of a piece of muscle, for these white blood cells lead a somewhat independent life even while they are in the body.

50

EINSTEIN'S CREASE

The theories of space and time initiated by Professor Einstein of Berlin have given a new twist to the old problem of free-will and destiny. According to Einstein the three dimensions of space, that is, up-down, right-left and backward-forward, form with the one dimension of time, that is, past-future, a four-dimensional system in which things are tracks and events are the junctions of these tracks. A moving particle of matter makes a sort of crease or ridge through the system, and this more or less interferes with the free motion of all other particles in the vicinity. For instance, the tracks of two oranges, cast out into empty space, tend to run together in the course of time, or, to use the Newtonic nomenclature, the two bodies are drawn together by the force of gravitation. One orange, alone in the universe, might conceivably roll around anyway at its own sweet will. But its absolute and arbitrary independence ceases the moment another orange comes into existence. Only a solitary monad could be completely free, and it would lose its freedom the next instant, for whatever it did would determine what it must do. If for a moment it did nothing but stay still (that is, confined its movement to the time dimension), it would so have acquired the habit of indolence (otherwise inertia) that it would never move of itself through all eternity. Which is, as the reader will observe, merely another way of stating Newton's first law.

To illustrate, take a new flat unrumpled sheet of paper. You can fold that any way you please. It is just as easy to start a crease in one direction as another. It is a *tabula rasa*. Very well, shut your eyes and start a crease across the paper with your finger-nail at random. But just as soon as you 'have started the crease you have permanently warped the paper and forever limited the freedom of all other foldings. The paper no longer bends with equal ease in all directions. You might as well have run your crease in any other direction, but once started it tends to run in the same direction—just as a moving body tends to continue in a straight line through space. Any other crease tends to run into the channel of the first, or if it crosses the first it is bent or bothered at the junction.

Another illustration: On the level plains of western Kansas when I was a boy a wagon could go anywhere. It could head straight for the cloud-like tip of Pike's Peak with the determination to get there or bust. But after one prairie-schooner had passed over the velvet sod of buffalo-grass all ways were not equal. The next wagon had a tendency to follow in the track of the first either because the wheels or the driver's mind ran most readily in a rut. After a while the random trail had worn into a road so deep that the driver had to have great determination and much swearing to get the horses out of it.

It seems to be so in everything. The start settles the sequence. What has been determines what shall be. Yesterday dictates to-day.

You sit down at the piano to compose a tune. You can strike any key you choose. But having struck one, the next will necessarily bear some relation to the first, and by the time you have struck half a dozen you settled the key to which you must conform under penalty of violating the natural laws of harmony. For music is mathematical, and the final chord is predestined when the first chord is sounded, however the melody may flow between. When an algebraic problem is once started the solution is settled, whatever may be the method of working it out.

Start a bonfire on a calm day. You may blow the flame from any side. But once going, the fire itself determines the direction of the wind that feeds it.

In making new compounds in the laboratory the chemist sometimes gets an oil or gum that he cannot crystallize. If the compound has been made before, he may go to the bottle in the stock-room and get a crystal to seed his solution. As soon as the minutest fragment of the crystal is dropped in, even an invisible dust particle, the whole solution crystallizes out instantly. But if the compound is a new one the chemist tries all sorts of tricks with the sticky stuff. He scratches it with a glass rod. He shakes it. He shocks it by sudden cooling. He drops in various kinds of crystals in the hope that one of them may be so much like the crystals of the unknown as to fool it into solidifying just as a hen is fooled into laying by a china egg. If by any of these means or by sheer accident the chemist can get a single microscopic crystal he can make pounds of it, tons of it. For instance glycerin, discovered in 1779, was known only in the liquid form until 1867, when certain crystals appeared spontaneously, and from them crystals of glycerin have been propagated ever since. Sometimes a substance has two different forms of crystallization. In that case the whole dishful will crystallize out in the form of whichever crystal is dropped into the solution or happens to get started first.

A white rat appears unexpectedly in a litter of brown ones. Nobody knows why it came, but once in existence it may become the primogenital parent of a new race of white rats. Possibly the first man was merely a monkey mutant.

What started the cyclone that has destroyed the city? Perchance a lady's fan or a falling leaf. It is useless to inquire, for its origin, whatever it may be, is too trivial to consider. All we can do, now that the wind is blowing, is to measure its velocity, map its movement, and endeavor to forecast its course.

So with everything in nature. Origins always elude us, possibly because they are too minute for our minds. Anyhow, if we could know them they would not help us to understand the world as it now runs. Did the first particle of matter move in a straight line or just dodge around like a mad hornet? Were the first couple of particles attractive or repellent to one another? We do not know, and it does not matter that we do not know. It appears that for the last few million years or more all particles have shown a disposition to travel straight and to draw together and we may safely assume that they will keep up these habits during the lifetime of the human race. Many of our statutory laws are, as we know, merely customs codified. Perhaps natural laws are the same. The universe might maybe have been warped some other way in its primeval and plastic state; but it was not, and we have only to deal with things as they are. Whether there was in the beginning any element of pure freedom, that is to say, of mere chance, it has long ago been lost in the complexities of the interrelations of all things. Now we live in an orderly universe, very fortunately for us, for otherwise we should go crazy from vain guessing at what would happen next.

Such are the reflections suggested by the new theory of gravitation. But don't blame Einstein for them. He merely started the crease along which my thought flowed.

51

The Success of a Failure

"No," said the lumber dealer, "your boy is good for nothing in my business. In fact, he is the most miserable failure I have ever seen and will never amount to anything."

"Well," replied the disappointed father, "since Emil is too stupid to make a living in lumber, I suppose I might as well let him go to college as he wants to."

So Emil Fischer went to Bonn University to study chemistry. Here he was recognized as one of the most brilliant and industrious students in the laboratory, and by the time he was twenty-three he had discovered a key that unlocked one of the most mysterious processes of life. This key was a coal-tar compound known to chemists as "phenyl hydrazine." It was both fortunate and fatal to Fischer. It made him one of the most famous chemists in the world, and it brought him disease and death. For the fumes of it are poisonous, and constant working with it ruined his health, as he realised it would.

But nothing could impair his energy or dampen his ardor. After he got free from the lumber business and started on his own track, he pursued it for forty-five years without interruption or diversion. As one of his colleagues said at the time of his death in 1919:

A life is ended in which there was no failure, no let-up in restless activity, no long groping about for something to accomplish. After one quick, clear vision of the goal the path led straight to its accomplishment, a chain of brilliant successes.

How Professor Fischer himself looked at his life-work is shown by these words:

Still more enticing to some, among whom I include myself, is the hope to climb up out of the valleys to those passes seen afar off, which lead to vast and as yet unexplored countries.

The unexplored country that he had in view and ventured in was no less than the formative functions of vegetable and animal life. With the aid of phenyl hydrazine he was able to solve the secret of sugar. Not content with finding out how sugar may be made by the plant, he learned to make it himself. He found it possible to produce in the laboratory many more kinds of sugar than can be discovered in nature. Finally, he worked out a process by which he could start with plain coal and water and build up a series of edible sugars.

Then Fischer tackled a still more difficult problem in nutrition, the constitution of the proteins. These form an essential part of our food, since they contain the nitrogen necessary to all life. It used to be thought that the proteins, whether of vegetable origin, like the gluten of wheat, or of animal origin, like the casein of milk, were much alike and that it made little difference which of the many we got in our food. But Fischer showed that a protein molecule was made up of a long chain of carbon and nitrogen compounds and that the links were of very different kinds. Finally, he made a sort of artificial protein, what might be called a laboratory beefsteak, but whether it was good to eat or not could not be determined, since there was so little of it and it cost so much. He spent $250 for the material alone, to say nothing of his time, in constructing this compound, and so, as he said, "it has not yet made its appearance on the dining table."

There is little prospect that the food of the future will come from the laboratory instead of the field. Even a professor of chemistry cannot live as cheaply as a corn-stalk. But the work of Fischer on the sugars and proteins has already been of immense value to the world in leading to the newer knowledge of nutrition, which is already being applied to the feeding of stock and people.

As Sir Henry Roscoe, professor of chemistry at Manchester, said of Fischer when he was awarded the Faraday medal, "His name has the sweetest of tastes in the mouth of every chemist." Fischer conquered for chemistry a field formerly claimed by biology. He brought within the reach of laboratory experimentation what had been regarded as the exclusive province of vital processes.

So it seems that a man may be a miserable failure as a lumber merchant and yet make a success of something else. The problem of education is to fit square pegs into round holes without whittling them down too much in the process of schooling.

52

Iron Nerves

When I opened the door I thought I had got in the wrong room. In the main laboratory building at Woods

Hole the biologists are confined to the separate cells along the corridor like the—well, like the monks in an ancient monastery. And they are all quite as devoted —if not all quite as devout—as any religious cenobite. You may find one giving his life to the study of sea-urchin eggs, and his neighbor in the next cubicle may be absorbed in microscopic molds.

The man I was after was a physiologist, Dr. R. A. Spaeth of Johns Hopkins, who, I was told, was making some interesting experiments on how nerves act. But when I opened the door I saw fine wires strung around the room and suspended in coils from the ceiling. There was electrical apparatus on the table, and I smelled the fumes of nitric acid in the air.

So I supposed that I had entered a chemical or electrical laboratory instead of one devoted to the in-vestigation of nervous action. But here was Dr. Spaeth dipping piano-wires into test-tubes of nitric acid and watching how they dissolve in the hope of solving the baffling question of nerve conduction.

This is a curious case of the siege-tactics of science. They are the same as military tactics. If the scientist finds that a direct attack on the main front does not bring him to the heart of the mystery he hunts around for an easier slope on some other side. How a nerve can carry a message has always been one of the most baffling mysteries of science. If you stick your finger into a match-flame a message of pain is telegraphed up to the brain, and back comes an order from headquar-ters on another line to contract the muscles of the finger and pull it out of the fire. The reply is prompt unless you are absent-minded, that is, unless central is asleep at the switchboard. But it is not instantaneous. The messages do not travel nearly so fast as the electrical impulse along a telegraph-wire. The speed for a nerve-impulse in man is about 140 yards a second, and that is about five times faster than a frog's nerves can carry a message. It is quicker at high temperatures than at low. This would point to a chemical process, for heat speeds up chemical reactions.

Twenty years ago Professor Ostwald of Leipzig pointed out that nerves in their alternation of active and passive states behaved something like iron in nitric acid. This hint was not followed up and was forgotten in 1920 when Dr. R. S. Lillie independently hit upon the same idea and worked out some interesting analogies.

Iron behaves very curiously in nitric acid. Stick the end of a piece of wire into a tube containing weak acid and it speedily dissolves. Bubbles of gas stream up, and in a minute the wire has completely disappeared in the liquid. You would naturally suppose that if you used acid less diluted with water the wire would dissolve quicker. But when you drop a wire into strong nitric acid there is no action! It begins to dissolve but suddenly stops, never to go again. That part of the wire that has been stuck into the liquid has become immune to the action of the acid. It has gone into some sort of a passive state that prevents its dissolving.

Now here comes in the most remarkable thing about it. The rest of the wire that has not yet entered the acid has also become passive! If you fill a deep tube with strong nitric acid and dip into it the end of a long wire, bubbles will at first come off, showing that the iron is beginning to dissolve, but soon this ceases. Now lower the rest of the wire into the acid and you will be amazed to see that the fresh sections of the wire as they enter the acid are not attacked like the first but are immune to the acid. Yards of the wire may be coiled up in the tube of acid and will remain there indefinitely without dissolving if let alone. If let alone, I say, for if you scratch one end of the wire, or touch it with some other metal such as zinc or copper, it becomes active again, and you can see the impulse of activity marked by its train of bubbles passing along the wire from one end to the other. Then the "iron nerve" becomes passive again. But a few minutes later it is ready for a second performance, and so on as long as the wire lasts. Pinch the end of the wire between your finger-nails as you might pinch a cat's tail, and the messages pass to the other end as it does along a nerve. Except that the cat's reaction is quicker.

If a series of iron wires is laid end to end and one of them is stimulated, a wave of energy passes all along the series, leaping from wire to wire, but so slowly that it can easily be followed by the eye.

Passive iron thus affords the most significant comparison to nerve conduction that has yet been discovered by physiologists. The iron's activity is much slower than that of the nerve. It is as though one were watching the passage of nervous stimulation under the influence of a stiff shot of hashish, or some other drug that lengthens the time-sense uncannily. Moreover, the iron fatigues in a way that nerves do not. Nerve fatigue has never been demonstrated. Apparently nerves recover instantaneously.

The jellyfish, for example, has its nervous system around the edge of its "umbrella." If you shock a jellyfish at one point in its circular nervous system, waves of activation immediately set out in both directions. The two waves presently meet and wipe each other out. E. Newton Harvey, working with a large jellyfish in the Tortugas Islands, managed to block one of these waves so that the nerve energy could travel in only one direction. It went continuously for eleven days and would undoubtedly be going still if the jellyfish hadn't died then.

Similarly, if one provided a loop of sufficient lengths of iron wire so that the first would have time to recover by the time the electrochemical wave reached the last, these truly "iron waves" would go on transmitting a single stimulating impulse until the wire was completely decomposed.

53

Science from the Side-Lines

The method of science is economy of thought. The aim of science is control of the future. A science arises from some human need and returns to earth to satisfy some—often some other—human need. It may soar so high into the empyrean as to be out of our sight, but it always comes back in the course of time bringing food like Elijah's raven.

So do not believe a mathematician when he boasts that his newly discovered theorem is of no possible use to anybody. Before he knows it some "base me-

chanical'' will snatch it out of his hand and use it in
the shops. No occupation seemed idler than the study
of geometry of four dimensions when anybody could
see that there are only three, yet now all of a sudden
the symbols of the fourth dimension appear in astro-
nomical and physical calculations and are likely to get
into chemistry and biology soon.

One cannot, of course, become a scientist by merely
reading science, however diligently and long. For a
scientist is one who makes science, not one who learns
science. A novelist is one who writes novels, not one
who reads them. A contortionist is one who makes con-
tortions, not one who watches them. Every real scientist
is expected to take part in the advancement of science,
to go over the top at least once in his life; when he
takes his Ph.D. degree, if never again. But of course
the number of those who are in reserve or in training
must always outnumber those at the front.

The highest reward of science, the secret satisfaction
of standing where no mortal man has ever stood before,
is rightly reserved to those who contribute most to its
advance. The pure thrill of primal discovery comes
only to the explorer who first crosses the crest of the
mountain range that divides the unknown from the
known. But if we cannot all feel that thrill to the full
we can at least catch a resonance of it in our own souls
by reading about it, as we know something of how
Balboa felt when he stared at the Pacific from a peak
in Darien, as well as how Keats felt on first opening
Chapman's Homer. The lives of explorers are always
exciting, whether they penetrate to the heart of Africa
like Livingstone or to the heart of the atom like Bohr.

At a baseball game there may be five thousand specta-
tors and only one man at the bat, but don't imagine he
is the only one having any fun. He alone can feel the
whack on the wood that tells him that he has made a
three-base hit, but the five thousand participate by
proxy in his pleasure as their muscles tense and their
pulses quicken.

There is also fun to be found in sitting on the side-
lines of science and watching the international game.
Those who are not musicians may get delight from
music, those who are not architects from architecture,
those who are not cooks from food. It is not necessary
to be a scientist to get pleasure and profit from scientific
researches. This is not a faculty confined to a few. It
is common to all who have any capacity for intellectual
enjoyment, and those who do not avail themselves of
it are curtailing their opportunities for happiness.

54

In Defense of Fireplaces

One of the considerable differences between British
and American customs is in the matter of house-heating.

The deviation was started out by that patriotic
scientist, old Ben Franklin, famous as the inventor of
the Franklin stove. From this beginning America has
developed most elaborate and perfect heating systems
by which a thousand rooms can be kept at an even
temperature all the year round.

On the other hand, the British have stuck to their

open fireplaces, cumbrous, dirty, wasteful, and, as it seems to us, uncomfortable. Americans, returning from a foreign tour, rejoice in the genial atmosphere of their apartments and declare, "This is the first time I have felt warm since I left home." The British fireplace roasts one side of the body while leaving the other side to freeze. One must revolve before it as on a perpendicular spit to give all sides an even chance, and even then the air is chilly and damp to breathe. It makes one shiver the more to see all that hot air escaping up the big chimney, when it is so much needed to warm the room.

We Americans have been disposed to attribute the retention of the inadequate and inconvenient fireplace to British backwardness and indifference to comfort. But now it seems that the British have some scientific justification for their preference besides personal prejudice and native conservatism.

To begin with, the fireplace is not so wasteful as it seems to be. An investigation made in Manchester of all sorts of coal-fired grates showed the best gave out twenty-four per cent and the worst twenty per cent of the heat of the fuel consumed. A gas fireplace is twice as good, for its efficiency of radiation is fifty per cent of the net heat value of the gas consumed. Besides this advantage, gas is a more economical way of using coal, since in gas-making the ammonia and tar are saved and coke is obtained. An electrical heater is best of all, since it sends out seventy-five per cent of the energy of the current in radiant heat and light.

Another point in favor of the fireplace is that radiant heat has been found to have certain physiological advantage over warm air from a steam-heating apparatus. Heat can be conveyed in two ways:

First, it can be carried by a current of hot air. This is called "convection."

Second, it can go by itself as ether-waves. This is called "radiation."

In the case of radiation no air or any other medium is necessary. The sun's rays come to us through ninety-three million miles of empty space without heating it or lighting it in the least. So, too, any glowing body, such as a bed of hot coal or a gas-log or an incandescent electric wire, gives off radiations that travel straight across the room without heating the air much although they heat up any solid body they may strike. But what we call a steam radiator would be more properly described as a steam-coil air-heater, for most of the heat we get from it comes to us in currents of warmed air.

Now, the Englishman, rightly or wrongly, does not want warm air. He wants cool air and a hot grate. He does not want an even temperature and a still atmosphere. He wants an uneven temperature and drafts. Professor W. A. Bone, chairman of the Fuel Economy Committee, stated the British ideal clearly in his report to the Association for the Advancement of Science meeting at Hull when he said:

The more nearly the conditions under which our living rooms are warmed and ventilated approach those of a warm summer's day—a cooling breeze blowing around the head, the varying sunshine warming one side of the body and the warm ground for the feet—the more comfortable and healthful they will be. The desirability of such conditions, which may be contrasted with the warm air of rooms heated by convection from steam coils, probably explains the Englishman's decided preference for the radiation from an open fireplace during our dreary British winters over the various forms of central heating which are favored in America and other countries where the winters are colder but brighter.

Professor Bone is kind enough to allow us a loophole for our preference in a difference of climate. But it is evident that more is to be said on the side of radiation than we have considered.

Perhaps, also, we have gone too far in our endeavor to secure a uniform temperature without drafts, even where we have provided thorough ventilation and proper humidity in our big buildings.

Professor Huntington of Yale says that the hardest work and highest thinking of the world are done where the temperature is variable and winds are frequent. His argument seems to point to the conclusion that the more uncomfortable the climate the better off are the people. Perhaps the same applies to houses.

55

The Social Psychologist Is Coming

The various sciences seem to be widening their outlook. The botanist who used to be content with a type specimen in his herbarium now takes to the open and talks of the sociology of the vegetable kingdom. The psychologist has ceased to be absorbed in the contemplation of the Ego and has taken up the observation of the Alter. He has discovered that the Socratic rule, "Know thyself!" does not involve a knowledge of other people. As Christianity expanded from the salvation of one's soul to the salvation of society, so now psychology is turning from introspection to circumspection.

I use the word "circumspection" here in its original sense of "looking around," but the psychologists are likely also to need it in its secondary sense of "looking out," for as soon as they leave their laboratories and go into the shop, the church, the hospital, and the legislature they will surely make trouble for somebody and so get into trouble themselves. I venture to prophesy that in the future psychology will be a storm-center just as evolution, higher criticism, and economics have been in the past, and that the professor who is suspected of having "unsound ideas" on, say, the relation of reaction-time to fatigue in industry, or on the rating of intelligence tests in appointments, or on the influence of the unconscious in popular moral standards, may be made to feel the weight of administrative discipline or of public indignation. But the social psychologist is coming just the same, and he will insist on having his say in the affairs of the family and the nation.

It may as well be publicly understood that scientists in general are getting tired of being called into consultation on affairs of state only after statesmen have made a muddle of them. The chemist was ignored until after the war broke out; then Washington wired him to come, and he was merely asked, "What is the quickest way to kill people?" The chemist responded promptly, "High explosives and poison gas." Washington said,

"Make them," and the chemist did. But the chemist does not now get due credit for his patriotic efforts in this emergency. On the contrary, he finds himself in bad odor—worse odor than usual—because he did his bit with such alarming proficiency.

Nobody at Washington thinks now of calling a conference of psychologists to tell, "What is the cause of this mysterious cloud of misunderstandings, this spirit of suspicion, this revival of old hatreds and stirring of new strifes, that seems likely to involve the world again in war or reduce it to chaos?"

Probably if the psychologist were called upon to answer such a question he would not be able to give as quick and correct a response as did the chemist. That is because the psychologist does not know his business as well as the chemist does his—not yet. Some day he may, and I hope he will soon; for really it is dangerous for the chemist to get so far ahead of the psychologist. A boy is dangerous if he learns how to pull a trigger long before he learns when to pull a trigger.

56

How Words Lose Reputation

Language is a circulating medium, as money is, and words, like coins, are apt to lose their value in the course of time. A decline in the exchange rating of a word may be due either to inflation, that is, too promiscuous application, or to discredit, that is, a growing popular suspicion of the soundness of its backing.

The Seven Wise Men of early Greece were called "sophists" as an honorific appellation. But later a "sophist" came to mean a man who pretended to know more than he did or, worse, who sold his wisdom to the highest bidder for the basest of purposes, that of making a wrong cause seem right.

Pythagoras repudiated the title of sophist, or wise man, because as he said, "none is wise save God." So he devised and assumed the more modest-sounding term of "philosopher," a lover of wisdom. But this term has narrowed, if not degenerated. Philosophy, once the sum total of human knowledge, has come, in common parlance, to be confined to speculative and abstract theory. When Plato said that states should be ruled by philosophers he did not mean that they should be ruled by professors of metaphysics.

This degenerative process has gone so far that we have no word in good repute and common usage to apply to a group of competent and learned men. The word "scholars" would once have served, but this has fallen from its high estate and come to mean "pupils," that is, those who are being schooled, instead of those who have been schooled. To call a man a "sage" calls up in the average mind the picture of something gray and pedantic, if not green and aromatic. The word "scientist" has become so narrowed and lowered and misapplied that men of science hesitate to use it longer. The titles of "professor" and "expert" are also distinctly losing caste. To call a man a "fellow" is not safe nowadays outside of the campus of a university.

It is hard to arrest a word when it is on the down grade and almost impossible for a word to regain a reputation once lost. It seems that some sort of gravitational force prevails in linguistics. The dictionary is crowded with words that once moved in the highest circles but now are outcast and marked "obs." or "vul."

The man who knows comes in the course of time to be considered a "knowing man," with the suspicion of knowing too much for his neighbors. The "kenning man" becomes the "cunning man." A master of arts gets the reputation of being "artful." A craftsman is regarded as "crafty." A politician has come to mean—well, a politician.

Four hundred years ago the word "virago" meant a heroic woman and was esteemed a fitting name to apply to Eve, the mother of all living. Nowadays no one would dare call a woman a virago to her face if she were one. "Hussy" has degenerated in a hundred years from a thrifty "housewife" to quite the opposite.

In Australian newspapers to-day you may see a lonely bachelor advertising for "a homely wife," not because he has an aversion to feminine beauty, but because he desires domesticity.

A "wretch" was not at all wretched on the start. *Othello* calls his beloved *Desdemona* "Excellent wretch." A modern maiden would not feel complimented by such a term of endearment.

A "prude" was merely a prudent person.

A "villain" and a "boor" once meant simply a countryman, not necessarily wicked or even rude. A "Knave" was a simple servant. A "varlet" was a candidate for knighthood. A "miscreant" meant one who differed from you in theology.

In 1548 it was proper to express the pious wish "that his son, Prince Edward, that good imp, may long reign over you." How is it that "imp" has since come to mean a little devil?

So, as we see, words generally degenerate as they grow old. That does not matter much, for we can always make new words so long as the alphabet holds out. I am not concerned over the loss of a name, but I am with the loss of the type that the name once signified. If an ancient and honorable title falls into disrepute it is not altogether without reason. It means that some at least of those who bore it have not lived up to its true meaning.

It would be a profitable exercise to consider such cases as occur to us of words that we see are gradually becoming lowered or limited and try to discover the cause of their decline and how it may be prevented.

57

HIGHWAYS OF KNOWLEDGE

The first need of a backward country is better communications, roads and railroads, telegraphs, and telephones, so that the separated settlements of the wilderness can get into touch with each other.

This world is a wilderness, scattered oases of civilization in vast areas of ignorance. Thinkers are few and far apart. Intercommunication of ideas is retarded, often stopped altogether, by the barrier of language, as traffic is interfered with by a change of rail gage at the frontier. Even in the same country minds of different training fail to gear. It does not matter so much if we do not know "how the other half lives," but it is of the highest importance that we know how the other half thinks, especially that small fraction of humanity which is thinking for the next century, namely, scientific investigators.

The amount of knowledge accumulated during the last three hundred years since man began the systematic investigation of nature looks large compared with the ignorance that preceded, but looks small when we compare it with what nobody yet knows. What is worse, this precious and painfully acquired knowledge is contained in a few small and perishable packages. I do not mean books; I mean brains. We say "knowledge is power," but the knowledge that lies in libraries has no more power than unmined coal. Can that be called "knowledge" which nobody knows? If all the books in the world were suddenly destroyed, how much learning would be left? And how many heads would be holding it?

Professor J. Arthur Thomson of the University of Aberdeen puts the point in his usual effective fashion when he says in his book on "The Control of Life":

When we think of the more effective and less wasteful exploration of the earth, or of gathering the harvest of the sea, or of making occupations more wholesome, or of beautifying human surroundings, or of exterminating infectious diseases, or of raising the health-rate, or of improving the physique of the race, or of recognizing the physiological side of education, we are amazed at the non-utilization of valuable —though confessedly incomplete—scientific knowledge.

Much has been done, but it must be confessed that man has been slow to follow science in the possession of his kingdom. Part of the reason is that we have not become accustomed, except in some directions, e.g., medical treatment, *to believe in science;* but a great part of the reason is a deficiency of character, that we do not care enough, that we lack resolution.

That is plain speaking and goes to the bottom of the difficulty. It is "deficiency of character, that we do not care enough" to even learn what little has been learned about the management of matter and especially the management of mankind. Science may be discovered by the few but it has to be applied by the many.

Waste of energy, waste of natural resources, waste of life, waste of time, all forms of waste go back to the waste of ideas. For there is already enough wisdom in the world to make the whole human race more comfortable, healthy, and prosperous than any individuals have so far been. But no country is yet thoroughly civilized, even from the standpoint of our present knowledge. To bring that about we must bridge the rivers of ignorance and hew highways through the jungles of superstition.

58

MAN AND THE MACHINE

On hearing craftsmen talk together about the inferiority of the machine, one is reminded of the sort of conversation which takes place between two pedestrians when an automobile passes, throwing dust and

the smell of gasolene in their faces. They talk then of
the value of walking as an exercise, its greater safety
and the opportunity it affords for the leisurely contemplation of nature, yet not withstanding the truth-
fulness of the remarks and the enthusiastic tone in
which they are uttered each is suspicious that the other
is insincere, secretly wishing that he were in the van-
ishing vehicle instead of trudging along the road.
There is undeniably a joy in doing things for oneself,
but there is a still greater joy in making others do
them—horses, slaves, machines. It is the delight of
mastery, the conquering of material by the hands, by
tools, and by machines. A man's joy of work comes
when he can use a tool as though it were a finger of
his hand, and a machine as though it were a tool.

It is a pleasure to use one's own legs, a greater pleasure to drive a horse or two horses or four horses, and
still greater to drive a forty-horse-power motor. Why
does the farmer-boy like to run the mowing-machine
better than to use the scythe? It is not so much because it is easier on his back, but because it is a more
triumphant occupation. He is accomplishing more, and
he feels more truly alive as he manages the horses,
raises and lowers, starts and stops, the sickle-bar, and
keeps his ears set to catch the slightest deviation in the
rhythm of each click and rattle of the machine he
rides.

The essential thing is that the man be great enough
to master the machine. When, as often in our modern
factories, he is a mere attendant upon the machine, his
work becomes slavery. Bigger machines continually
demand bigger men to run them.

It is not true that machine products need be monotonous. The machine may be made to do man's work just as he wants it done, smooth or rough, even or uneven, regular or irregular. It is easier to have a machine do its work with artistic inexactness than with mathematical precision. It is often necessary only to loosen a screw, and the product will resemble the best hand-made. Protographers worked for years to secure depth of focus. They went to great trouble and expense to make lenses which will give an equally sharp definition to near and far objects. By and by it was suggested that they were on the wrong track; that a certain haziness and fusion of lines was more beautiful. At once, by a simple turn of the wrist, the matter was remedied. The front lens was loosened up a bit, and modern art photography was born. The adding-machine in the bank does its work with mathematical exactness, but it need not be so. If desired, a machine could be constructed so that it would make a mistake in adding its nine hundred and thirtieth column of figures, and immediately reform and lead a life of exemplary correctness ever after. As for the lack of adaptation to the individual, it is true that factory chairs, made to fit the average man, are often ill adapted to the conformation of the exceptionals; but, so far as I am acquainted with it, art furniture is not made to fit any human being, average or exceptional.

The art-and-crafts people are too much inclined to put methods above results, and to praise good intentions rather than achievement. So long as a man is making something for his own amusement no one has a right to criticize him; but as soon as he demands a

higher price for it in the market on the ground that he
had more fun making it, the public will challenge this
method of valuation. In so far as training in handi-
craft teaches one to appreciate beautiful objects it is
an excellent thing. But I have known some cases
where "the clean, clear joy of creation" so intoxicated
a man that he thought his own mud hut was better than
somebody else's Parthenon. Artisans ought to be more
altruistic and recognize a good thing when they see it,
even if done by another or by a soulless machine.

The lady who makes a purple cow on a sofa-pillow
has as much of the joy of creation as Michelangelo when
he carved his Moses; probably more, for she comes
nearer attaining her artistic ideal. The shaky-table
people are altogether too numerous now and not in
need of further encouragement in their mistaken efforts.
Don't shoot at the pianola; I am very positive that
there would be more good music in my neighborhood
if 199 out of the 200 who are now trying to play on
the piano would use that ingenious machine. The chief
value of the invention is that it affords an infallible
method of distinguishing between those people who love
to hear good music and care nothing how it is produced,
and those who profess to love music, when really all
they admire is the manual dexterity and patient efforts
of their personal friends. "An ill-favored thing, but
mine own," was the feeling of *Touchstone,* but, then
Touchstone was a fool. We want to rid the earth of
people who take delight in doing things poorly.

The claim of the superiority of hand-made products
might pass unchallenged were it not that our suspicions
are aroused by the fallacious and adventitious argu-

ments advanced by the artful and crafty folks. Instead of letting the products speak for themselves, they commend them upon other grounds than their own merit, even adducing in their favor such faults as their labor-cost and their resemblance to antiques. Is linen made with uneven threads more beautiful than the smooth finish? Very well, then, make it so, by machine if you can, by hand if you cannot, just because it is more beautiful, not because it is like that which our grandmothers wove. And don't compliment the dear old ladies on their superior artistic sense, for they probably wet the linen with their tears because they could not get it smoother. The modern craftsman esteems it a triumph of art when he can imitate the ancient craftsmen's blunders.

59

SHARK-TOWED SUBMARINES

Great Britain's determination to remain mistress of the seas has been made plain by legislation, poetry, and action for the last four hundred years. It is only a few years since as her associate in the late war we joined in the singing of

> Rule Britannia! rule the waves!
> All thine shall be the subject main,
> And every shore it circles thine.

But it is not so commonly known that one of the proposed methods by which Great Britain was to hold her supremacy of the seas was the use of submarines towed by sharks. The inventor of this ingenious scheme was Dr. Erasmus Darwin, grandfather of Charles, who derived more than one hint for his theory of evolution from Erasmus Darwin's volume of versified science, "The Botanic Garden."

The most famous passage in this curious work is that in which Erasmus Darwin anticipates the automobile, the steam-tug, and the airplane:

> Soon shall thy arm, unconquered Steam! afar
> Drag the slow barge, or drive the rapid car;
> Or on wide-waving wings expanded bear
> The flying-chariot through the fields of air.
> Fair crews triumphant, leaning from above,
> Shall wave their fluttering 'kerchiefs as they move;
> Or warrior-bands alarm the gaping crowd,
> And armies shrink beneath the shadowy cloud.

This is a good guess for 1789, although it is not steam but gasolene that we are using for automobiles and airplanes. But Grandfather Darwin could not anticipate the internal-combustion engine, and he knew that steam would not work under water, and so when he undertook to describe a submarine he could not see how the boat could be propelled unless fish could be harnessed to it. So he wrote:

> Led by the Sage, lo! Britain's sons shall guide
> Huge *Sea-Balloons* beneath the tossing tide;
> The diving castles, roof'd with spheric glass,
> Ribbed with strong oak and barr'd with bolts of brass,
> Buoy'd with pure air shall endless tracts pursue,
> And Priestley's hand the vital flood renew,—
> Then shall Britannia rule the wealthy realms,
> Which Ocean's wide insatiate wave o'erwhelms:

> Confine in netted bowers his scaly flocks,
> Part his blue plains, and people all his rocks,
> Deep, in warm waves beneath the Line that roll,
> Beneath the shadowy ice-isles of the Pole,
> Onward, through bright meandering vales, afar,
> Obedient sharks shall trail her sceptered car,
> With harness'd necks the pearly flood disturb,
> Stretch the silk rein, and champ the silver curb.

Absurd as this is as science, and poor as it is as poetry, yet it has many points of interest. The author solved the question of submarine ventilation by the means now employed, that is, the renovation of the air by oxygen gas, which had been discovered only fifteen years before by his friend, Joseph Priestley, a preacher-chemist who was driven out of England and came to America because of his political and religious nonconformity.

But Erasmus Darwin made a bad guess in his surmise as to the motive-power of the future submarine. Man has never been able to train to harness any animals of the sea. His control stops with the shore.

And now he is getting ready to dismiss the ox and horse from their long servitude and rely instead upon the inanimate energy of fuel and falls to run his slow barges and rapid cars as well as his flying-chariot and sea-balloons.

60

MAN AFRAID OF NOTHING

Nothing frightens man so much as nothing. The idea of empty space is horrible to him. He abhors a vacuum.

If he can't find anything else to fill it with, he fills it with his imagination. Primitive man filled the space about him with fairies, ghosts, spirits, demons, invisible beings of all sorts, some of them grotesque or malignant, but anyhow company to him.

Man early fixed up a snug little universe according to his fancy, a bowl inverted on a plate, as mushrooms are served. Above the bowl were the gods who were pleasant to look up to, although their conduct was not always what it should be. Below the plate were demons, terrifying of course but better than nothing, for they were much like folks after all.

But when Galileo's telescope knocked to pieces this neat boxed-in cosmos man was scared out of his wits. At first he refused to believe it, and he does not like it yet. For he cannot bear to think of being stuck on the surface of a ball that is whirling around at the rate of a thousand miles an hour and traveling through empty space at the rate of a thousand miles a minute.

Chesterton expresses his aversion to the scientific view in these lines:

> The dear sun dwarfed of dreadful suns,
> Like fiercer flowers on stalk,
> Earth lost and like a little pea,
> In high heaven's towering forestry.

Man feels as lonely as *Robinson Crusoe*, thus cast away on a desert planet. There are no neighbors within call, perhaps none anywhere in the universe. The nearest habitation is over two hundred thousand miles away, and nobody lives there, not even lunatics. The next is Venus 25,700,000 miles off on the road to

the sun, while in the other direction the nearest planet
is Mars 48,600,000 miles away. The four big planets
farther out are too cold for comfort, three or four
hundred degrees below zero Fahrenheit, and besides
they are gaseous or at least so soft in substance that a
man would sink into them like water. The only other
planet, Mercury, is so close to the sun that it has a
temperature of 450 degrees which would melt the *Tin
Man*.

All of the planets, therefore, seem out of the question as the abode of life with the possible exception of
the two nearest to ours in space and nearest to ours in
size and state. But there is no evidence that either
Mars or Venus has water or oxygen enough to support
animal life of any sort. Some astronomers have reported a complicated system of irrigation ditches on
Mars, but others with equally good eyes and bigger
telescopes can see nothing of the sort. The mean temperature on Mars is probably about sixty degrees below
zero, and so most likely Mars has long ago lost the
higher forms of life if it ever had any.

Human life requires such a close adjustment of
chemical and physical conditions that there is small
chance of its finding suitable means of support anywhere else than upon the earth, and even here the favorable environment will not last forever. Even if the
climate of another planet should at some time have been
like ours, it would be highly improbable that the course
of evolution should have produced beings in the least
like ourselves.

Wells was doubtless right in supposing in his ''War
of Worlds'' that the Martians, if there were any, would

be at least as unlike us as are the devil-fish. And he
was also safe in assuming that if the Martians and we
got together there would be a fight.

But man is so constituted that he would rather wage
perpetual warfare with the hosts of other planets than
to know that he was living alone in an illimitable
universe.

61

MIND-CLEANING TIME

Housecleaning time, when every article of furniture
from cellar to garret is handled and dusted, occurs
traditionally each spring. An annual purification of
the spiritual nature, when we overhaul and furbish up
our morals, is set by all the churches. We are urged
by sanitarians to subject ourselves to periodic physical
examinations.

Yet it is quite as important to keep our minds in as
good condition as our houses, our consciences, or our
bodies. Error is as contagious as disease. A false
belief may make more trouble in the world than a wrong
intention.

Vacation is a good time to overhaul your brain from
the frontal lobe to the cerebellum. Review your axioms,
revise your postulates, and reconsider the unexpressed
minor premises of your habitual forms of logic. All
your reasoning, however correct, all your knowledge,
however great, may be vitiated by some fundamental
fallacy, carelessly adopted and uncritically retained.
Get a lamp and peer into all the dark corners of your
mind. No doubt you keep the halls and reception-

rooms that are exposed in conversation to your friends in fairly decent and creditable order. But how would you like to let them look into your cerebral garret and subliminal cellar, where the toys of childhood and the prejudices you inherited from your ancestors mold and rot?

Hunt out and destroy with great care every old rag of superstition, for these are liable at any time to start that spontaneous combustion of ideas we call fanaticism against which there is no insurance. The bigger the brain the more dangerous such things are, for they have the more fuel. A little decaying superstition in the mind of a great man has been known to conflagrate a nation.

Errors breed errors. They multiply like microbes, especially through neglect. A single false belief may infect all the sound facts you pile in on top of it. Better an empty room than a rubbish-heap. In the words of our American philosopher, Josh Billings, "it is better not to know so many things than to know so many things that are not so."

Go systematically through your intellectual equipment and see wherein it is deficient. Add annuals to your mental cyclopedia. Pick up each one of the sciences where you left off at school and bring it down to date. Look over the fields of art and literature to see what you have missed or misconceived. Don't let your sociology get too far behind the age. See that your philosophy and psychology bear the same date as the calendar. Examine your religious creed in the light of modern knowledge to see if it needs revision. Take down the atlas and consider how long it has been since you heard from each country. Visit the planets in turn. Take another view of ancient history through the telescope provided by modern scholarship.

This inspection of one's stock of ideas is necessary because they do not keep as if they were in cold storage. They do not remain unchanged when stored away and neglected. There is a lot of thinking going on in our brains that we do not know anything about. Ideas are apt to sprout or spoil, like potatoes in a cellar. Facts will ferment from yeasty thoughts until they intoxicate the brain. Falsehoods generate ptomaines, poisoning the mind and producing inexplicable disease and death. You can not be too careful. Clean out your mind at least once a year.

62

New Light on the Origin of Life

Was the first living being a plant or animal? How could either originate out of non-living matter?

These are questions that have hitherto baffled scientists. They could trace back, more or less satisfactorily, the lines of development of plants and animals to the simplest and most primitive forms of life, but there they ran up against an insurmountable wall, on the near side of which was the world of living organisms and on the far side the world of inert mineral and inorganic matter.

We all know that non-living matter can be converted over into living matter for we do that ourselves whenever we eat or breathe. We all know that green plants have the power of building up sugar and starch and wood (the so-called carbohydrates) out of the water of the soil and carbon dioxide of the air, for we can see them do it any sunny day. But it is life only that can bring into the living organism this inorganic material. Water and carbon dioxide, which is plain "soda-water," does not spontaneously change over into sugar or start to grow into a plant. It requires green colored granules of the leaves, called chlorophyl, to effect this trans-formation.

But chlorophyl is a very complicated chemical com-pound. It is formed only by green plants as they de-velop in the sun's rays from white sprouts. So the plant must exist before chlorophyl is formed. But on the other hand a plant could not exist unless it got its energy from the sugar and other stuff stored up previously by some chlorophyl-bearing plant. Even the simplest green plant cannot live and grow on its nutri-tive salts in the sunshine unless it has a bit of plant-stuff to feed on as a starter.

We might surmise as a way out of the dilemma that animal life came first on the earth and in decaying supplied the primitive plants with the necessary organic food-stuff. But here we are blocked because animals are parasites of plants. They live on the sugars and so forth that the green leaves have stored up by means of sunshine.

So this was the perplexing situation. Plants can feed on animals or other plants. Animals can feed on plants or other animals. But where could the first animals or plants get their food when there was nothing but mineral matter in the world? It was worse than the old question: which came first, the hen or the egg?

But of late we are beginning to get light on the problem. The wall between the living and non-living is crumbling down. Certain sugars and proteins, such as the plant forms that we eat, can now be made in the laboratory out of inorganic material. Artificial cells have been constructed that grow and crawl and feed themselves and stick out feelers and subdivide very much like living cells. It has been found that ultra-violet rays, that is, light of such short waves that it cannot be seen, can convert water and carbon dioxide into sugar as chlorophyl does.

Such short waves are not contained in the sunshine that reaches the earth to-day, but it is found that ordinary rays may act the same way in the presence of certain substances such as iron-rust in water. These energetic rays are also able to incorporate the nitrogen of mineral salts into compounds like the protein of the living cell. So here we see the possibility that the action of the sunlight on the sea in primordial periods —or even in the present—might produce sufficient food to give a single cell a start in life and enable it to grow and multiply and develop into other higher forms.

But how this primal cell got to going in this way the biologists are only beginning to surmise. Dr. E. J. Allen at the Hull meeting of the British Association for the Advancement of Science ventured the theory that the first organism was of the animal sort and spherical shape but that it gradually grew a tail or whip that enabled it to rise to the sunny surface of the sea whenever it sank below, and that it there acquired the chlorophyl by which it could make its own food out of the air and water. This is far from knowing what did happen in those early days, but it is a great advance to be able even to speculate as to how it might have happened, since not many years ago it seemed that it could not happen at all.

The old question of spontaneous generation has taken on a new aspect from the discovery in recent years of organisms too minute to be discerned by the most powerful microscopes. They may pass through porcelain filters that will catch ordinary bacteria, and so cannot be so very much greater than the largest protein molecules known to the chemist. Yet they are capable of infecting animals and plants with certain specific diseases, such as the mosaic diseases that discolor tomato and tobacco leaves. Here chemistry and biology come close together, and the chasm between them may some day be bridged. As Professor Dendy of the University of London says in "Problems of Modern Science":

In this more minute realm of the ultramicroscopic organisms or viruses the transition from the inorganic to the organic may conceivably be taking place even at the present time.

So it is evident that some scientists are coming to look upon the origin of life, not as a unique event in the history of the world, occurring under exceptional conditions in the remote past, but as something which might occur or may be occurring to-day.

63

Making Medicines Hit the Mark

The primitive medicine-man prowled about the jungle by himself led by that insatiable curiosity characteristic of the scientist of all ages. Where the rest of his tribe saw only woods and weeds, his quick eye caught sight of a strange fruit or his sensitive nose detected the fragrance of an unfamiliar flower. He dug up roots and tasted them. If they tasted good he said, "That's a food." If they tasted bad he said, "That's a medicine."

The primitive medicine-man was the astronomer, botanist, mineralogist, and theologian of his tribe. He was chemist, drug manufacturer, dispenser, and physician all in one. He was also something of a psychologist. He interpreted dreams with the fluency of a Freudian, and he employed suggestive therapeutics in the most modern manner. He was in the widest sense of the words a general practitioner.

That the savage witch-doctor had in him the elements of a scientist is shown by his employment of deductive reasoning and inductive experimentation. Assuming that nature has provided a drug for every disease, he drew the deduction that for every drug nature must have provided a disease to correspond. So as he chewed a bitter leaf, bark, or berry he ruminated, "From the taste it is evident that the essential principle is a glucoside of some toxic alkaloid with a name ending in *-in*." I do not know the language that this primitive medicine-man spoke, and so I am translating his meditation into modern English. "Here," he thought, "is a medicine of some sort. What disease is it designed to cure? I can only find out by trying." So he set out to find a patient on whom to experiment.

When he found one who was sufficiently sick to be helpless he dosed him with a decoction of the queerest looking roots and the most aromatic barks and most acrid seeds that he could find. He administered salts scraped from the alkali-beds and watched the effect. He made ointments and salves for the wounded. Sometimes he put the salve on the wound, and sometimes he put it on the sword that caused the wound. He observed, quite correctly, that one seemed to work as well as the other.

I am bringing this ancient history before you for two reasons: first, that you may give proper honor to the prehistoric practitioners of the chemist's art and, second, that we may consider how we can improve upon his practice. This old hit-or-miss method of experimentation carried on for thousands of years was a painful process for the patients, however profitable it may have been for the doctor. But out of it came in the course of time all the materia medica which the physician had to work with until, within the memory of the youngest of us, synthetic drugs began to be prepared. We are not yet freed from dependence upon the chance bounty of nature and the chance discoveries of savage scientists. But now such natural products are being supplemented and in some cases supplanted by artificial preparations of our own invention for specific purposes.

At any rate we can improve upon the research methods of the witch-doctor of antiquity, for instead of trying out new drugs recklessly on bedridden patients as he did, we can make use of white rats, rabbits, and guinea-pigs with little harm to them and with great benefit to humanity.

The aim of the pharmacologist is to make the medicine fit the disease as it was the aim of the *Lord High Executioner* of "The Mikado" "to make the punishment fit the crime." We now have drugs that can distinguish between friends and foes.

The protozoa are waging a war of extermination on the metazoa. Human beings, as the highest organisms, suffer from the attacks of the lowest. In the struggle for existence between man and the microbe, the weaker, minuter, inferior, but more numerous party always wins in the end.

But though we are engaged in a losing battle, we must keep up our courage and prevent our microscopic enemies from overpowering us as long as possible. In this conflict the drug-store is the arsenal and the drug manufacturer is the munition-maker. This is the chemical warfare branch of the national defense service in peace-time. Chemists are the defenders of our lives against foes more dangerous than those of the late war. Even during that conflict the Allies suffered more fatalities from the germs than from the Germans.

Now, success in chemical warfare, whether with munitions or medicinals, depends upon scientific research. The chemist is now busy inventing new weapons of attack and new means of defense, antiseptics and prophylactics. A microbe or parasite, although it may be inside the body, is as much a foreign foe as a mad dog. It must be shaken off or killed.

The day of the shot-gun dose has gone by. The modern doctor uses a rifle. In former times it often happened that the antiseptic was aimed at a bacillus and killed a phagocyte. Before the era of recent research the best of antiseptics was carbolic acid. Yet carbolic acid applied to a wound killed off the invaders and defenders of the bodily citadel with almost equal impartiality. This is as if the United States, entering the war in defense of France, had showered poison gas all along the front and wiped out both the German and French armies.

But the new germicides like acriflavine, malachite green, gentian violet, acid fuchsine, brilliant green, crystal violet, and methylene blue not only destroy the microbe invaders of the human system, but help instead of hindering its natural defenders, the phagocytes. These, as any one could tell by the names, are all dyes. A wounded man in the hospital nowadays looks like a camouflaged warship.

Disease is war; either an invasion of hostile hosts as in the case of tuberculosis or a local rising of insurgent cells as in the case of cancer. But war can never be ended by fighting, nor can disease be abolished by curative medicine. The world may never be freed from the danger of war nor the body from the danger of disease, but we begin to see how we may work to that end. A new era of promise has opened with the advent of synthetic pharmaceuticals.

64

How the Chemist Moves the World

The chemist provides the motive-power of the world, the world of man, not the inanimate globe. Archimedes said he could move the world if he had a long enough lever. The chemist moves the world with molecules. The chemical reactions of the consumption of food and fuel furnish the energy for our muscles and machines. If the chemist can only get control of the electron, he will be in command of unlimited energy. For in this universe of ours power seems to be in inverse ratio to size and the minutest things are mightiest.

When we handle particles smaller than the atom we can get behind the elements and may effect more marvelous transformations than ever. The smaller the building-blocks the greater the variety of buildings that can be constructed. The chemistry of the past was a kind of cooking. The chemistry of the future will be more like astronomy; but it will be a new and more useful sort of astronomy such as an astronomer might employ if he had the power to rearrange the solar system by annexing a new planet from some other system or expediting the condensation of a nebula a thousand times.

The chemist is not merely a manipulator of molecules; he is a manager of mankind. His discoveries and inventions, his economies and creations, often transform the conditions of ordinary life, alter the relations of national power, and shift the currents of thought; but these revolutions are effected so quietly that the chemist does not get the credit for what he accomplishes, and indeed does not usually realize the extent of his sociological influence.

For instance, a great change that has come over the world in recent years, and has made conditions so unlike those existing in any previous period that historical precedents have no application to the present problems, is the rapid intercommunication of intelligence. Anything that anybody wants to say can be communicated to anybody who wants to hear it anywhere in all the wide world within a few minutes, or a few days, or at most a few months. In the agencies by which this is accomplished—rapid transit by ship, train, or automobile, printing, photography, telegraph and telephone, wired or wireless—chemistry plays an essential part, although it is so unpretentious a part that it rarely receives recognition. For instance, the expansion of literature and the spread of enlightenment, which put an end to the Dark Ages, is ascribed to the invention of movable type by Gutenberg, or somebody else, at the end of the fourteenth century. But the credit belongs rather to the unknown chemist who invented the process of making paper. The ancient Romans stamped their bricks and lead pipes with type, but printing had to wait more than a thousand years for a supply of paper. Movable type is not the essential feature of printing, for most of the printing done nowadays is not from movable type but from solid lines or pages. We could if necessary do away with type and press altogether, and use some photographic method of composition and reproduction, but we could not do without paper. The invention of wood-pulp paper has done more for the expansion of literature than did the invention of rag paper six hundred years ago.

Print is only an imperfect representation of the sound of speech, a particularly imperfect representation in the case of English, because we cannot tell how half the words sound from their spelling. But the phonograph gives us sounds directly, and the audion and the radio have extended the range of a speaker until now a speaker may have an audience covering a continent and including generations yet unborn. What these inventions do for sound, photography has done for the sister sense of light. By means of them man is able to transcend the limitations of time and space. He can make himself seen and heard all round the earth and to all future years.

65

To Exchange: A Chemist for a Colony

The German chemists are trying to win back the colonies that the German kaiser lost. They are offering to trade a new coal-tar drug for the African territory which Germany held before 1914, but which fell to the victors of the Great War. This territory amounts to a million square miles, or one third of the area of the United States, and has been divided up by mutual agreement between Great Britain, France, Belgium, and Portugal. It comprises some of the richest and most fertile land on the globe, but it rests under a curse, the sleeping-sickness.

This mysterious malady, that has laid waste a large part of the Dark Continent, is now known to be due a minute parasite that lives in the blood of man and beast and is called a trypanosome. When you look at one through a microscope you would not think that so little a creature could have so long a name or do so much harm. It looks like a smashed mosquito wiggler or a stickless kite. It propels itself along by sculling with its whip-like tail. The tsetse-fly gets its living by sucking the blood of wild animals, cattle, and human beings, and in so doing peddles about the microbe from sick to well. There are various sorts of trypanosomes and blood-sucking flies, each having its own habits and routes; but anyhow the infected individual suffers at first from fever and gradually sinks into an insensibility, from which the sleeper rarely wakes. This sort of sleeping-sickness is peculiar to Africa and has nothing in common with the disease that has recently appeared in America except the name and somnolent symptom.

In the latter part of the last century when Europeans invaded the interior of Africa they found this microörganism the most dangerous of the wild animals to be combated. Lions and elephants could be killed; but the tsetse-fly was too small to be shot, and the trypanosome was too small to be seen. How to destroy the parasite without harming the host was the question.

The first sign of a solution of the problem came in 1904 when the German physician Ehrlich and his Japanese assistant Shiga discovered an aniline dye which, injected into the blood of a person seized with sleeping-sickness, would kill the parasite. This dye was named trypan red. Two years later Mesnil and Nicolle of the Pasteur Institute of Paris found that several similar dyes made by the Bayer Dye Works were also serviceable. These dye-drugs were all derivatives of naphthalene, familiar to us all, since little white balls of it drop from our clothes when we shake them out in the fall.

But none of the known dyes were sufficiently active so that they could be relied upon to clean out the pests from the body of the patient. The Bayer company has quietly continued its search for something more powerful and equally innocuous and has at last, after 204 compounds had been made and found unsatisfactory, got one that cures. It is not a dye but a white powder, soluble in water. It was tried successfully on mice, rats, guinea-pigs, rabbits, dogs, and horses, and finally upon man. An English patient who had suffered from sleeping-sickness for a year, and on whom all the customary remedies had been tried in vain, was cured by four doses amounting altogether to an eighth of an ounce. Better still, it is found that a single dose will make a person immune to the disease for a long period even if infected by the fly. It is also said that the new medicine or some of its relatives will cure malaria and other tropical fevers.

Bayer 205 does not contain arsenic like "606," which is used to destroy a similar blood parasite, but its exact composition is kept secret. Small samples of the drug have been furnished for experimentation to Belgian, British, and American physicians, but under pledge of professional secrecy. At a meeting in Hamburg of the German Association of Tropical Medicine one of the speakers said:

Bayer 205 is the key to tropical Africa, and consequently the key to all the colonies. The German Government must, therefore, be required to safeguard this discovery for Germany. Its value is such that any privilege of a share in it granted to other nations must be made conditional upon the restoration to Germany of her colonial empire.

It is indeed the irony of fate that the Germans should have found the means of making their colonies colonial-able only after they had lost them and that their discovery must go to benefit those who took their African territories from them. But this suggestion of buying back a million square miles for a single chemical symbol can hardly be taken seriously. The chemists of other countries are already hot on their trail and with what clues they have will doubtless eventually find out the composition of the mysterious medicine. But whether Germany makes anything out of it or not, it may turn out that her scientists by this discovery will bring as much benefit to Africa as her soldiers did damage in Europe.

66

THE ECLIPSE AND EINSTEIN

The development of a batch of photographic plates is often awaited with impatience and anxiety. In the case of amateur photography the impatience is manifested by the snap-shotter and the anxiety by his sitters.

But probably never before have so many people in all parts of the world been eager to learn "how the plates turned out" as in the case of those brought back from

THE EINSTEIN CAMERA IN THE AUSTRALIAN DESERT

In order to observe the solar eclipse of September 21, 1922, the Crocker Expedition, sent out by the Lick Observatory of the University of California, was stationed at Wallal on the almost uninhabited coast of Western Australia. Here it never rains, so the party had fair weather for observation, while the British, Dutch and German expeditions, which went to Christmas Island in the Indian Ocean, failed to get a single photograph since the sun was clouded over at the time of the eclipse. This picture shows the 15-foot camera used for photographing the stars during the eclipse, to discover the Einstein effect. At the left may be seen a bit of the supports of the 5-foot Einstein cameras and on the right the tower of the 40-foot telescope.

Australia by Dr. W. W. Campbell, director of the Lick Observatory and president of the University of California.

For these negatives were taken during the eclipse of September 21, 1922, and contained the evidence for or against the Einstein theory of relativity, which has excited the interest of all scientists and, for various reasons, an unexpectedly large proportion of the unscientific public. The less people could understand about it the more eager they were to hear about it.

The man who manifested the least anxiety over the result of the eclipse expedition was perhaps Einstein himself, for, having made up his mind eight years before how the heavenly bodies must behave, he remains serenely indifferent to the efforts of astronomers to find out how they do behave. It followed, as a logical deduction from his theory of the relativity of all measurements of space and time, that a ray of light passing close to the sun would be drawn out of its straight course as though the light were attracted by the presence of such a heavy mass. And since the path of the ray is drawn inward toward the sun an observer on the earth, looking back up the ray, would see the star as though it were moved outward from the sun. If a photograph of a group of stars taken with the sun in the middle is compared with a photograph of the same group without the sun, the images of the stars in the former case will therefore be seen to have been displaced from their ordinary positions in the sky. The star images nearest the sun will naturally be displaced the most and the others in proportion to their distance. The effect is the same as you have noticed when a patron

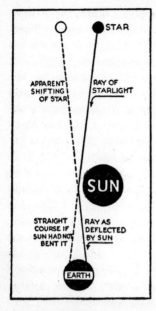

STAR

APPARENT SHIFTING OF STAR

RAY OF STARLIGHT

SUN

STRAIGHT COURSE IF SUN HAD NOT BENT IT

RAY AS DEFLECTED BY SUN

EARTH

HOW A LIGHT RAY IS DE-FLECTED BY SUN

According to Einstein's theory of relativity a ray of light passing close to the sun would be bent a little out of its straight course, as though it were attracted by such a heavy body. British and American astronomers observing recent eclipses report such a deflection. Of course in this diagram the angle of deflection and the size of the earth are much magnified while the distances and the size of the star are much mini-fied.

of the bootlegger gets aboard a crowded street-car. All move away from him, and those nearest the obnoxious individual move farthest. As figured out from Einstein's formula, a ray of starlight just grazing the sun's disk would be deflected to the extent of 1.75 seconds of arc.

Of course the stars cannot be photographed when the sun is shining into the telescope, and so one must wait till the sun is totally shielded from the earth by the moon. The first opportunity to put the Einstein theory to the test was the eclipse of 1919, and even while the war was on British astronomers were preparing expeditions to be sent to Brazil and western Africa to put Einstein to the proof. Professor Eddington of Cambridge, who was in charge of the expeditions, was convinced that his observations confirmed the relativity theory of gravitation. But his best plate contained only seven good star images, and this seemed to conservative scientists rather too slight a foundation to support so revolutionary a theory. Since the experiment could not be repeated until the next eclipse, astronomers and amateurs had to hold their breath for four years or waste it in vain disputes.

But when Professor Campbell explained to the American Philosophical Society of Philadelphia and the National Academy of Sciences in Washington the results of the Crocker Expedition to Australia, there was little ground left for skepticism on this point. Instead of one good plate with seven stars, he had four plates of the eclipse, each showing from sixty-two to eighty-four star images. To compare with these he had four plates of the same stars taken at night before the eclipse. The negatives are seventeen inches square, and it took Dr. Campbell fifty hours of working time to measure with the micrometer the positions of the stars on a single pair of plates. Dr. Trumpler repeated the measurements independently, and neither astronomer could know what the results would be until they were finally figured out. Check plates taken of other stars show that the displacement of the images could not be due to any defects of the telescope or of the sensitive plates.

The final average of all the measurements of all the star images on all the plates gave a deflection for a ray passing at the edge of sun's disk of 1.72 seconds of arc, almost exactly what Einstein had predicted and twice as great as could be deduced from the Newtonian theory of gravitation.

This does not mean, as some have hastily concluded, that "gravitation will be abolished." No, apples will still fall from trees as they did in the time of Newton.

So will boys, if they do not hold on tight. But it may mean that boys in college will have to study geometry of four dimensions instead of the plain and easy Euclid that they make such a fuss over. And it means that we elders will have to adjust our inelastic minds to ideas more revolutionary than those introduced into the world by Copernicus and Darwin.

67

THE FAITH OF THE SCIENTIST

The things we are surest about we do not talk about. We do not have to. There are certain things that all sensible men take for granted, and there is no use trying to convince those who are not sensible. But once in a while it is well to dig down to the very foundations of our faith to see what they are.

There is one principle that underlies all of the sciences as it does all ordinary life and yet is not often specifically pointed out.

This is the invariance of nature or the constancy of cause and effect; that under the same circumstances the same thing will happen always anywhere. This is a bit vague, for of course the circumstances are never twice the same all through the universe. And nobody can prove it or tell why it must be so.

For instance, who knows if the law of gravitation will hold true to-morrow? Why should not all particles of matter repel one another instead of attracting one another?

THE PHOTOGRAPHIC PLATE THAT CONFIRMED EINSTEIN'S THEORY

This is one of the photographs of the total eclipse of the sun, September 21, 1922, taken at Wallal, Western Australia, by the Crocker Expedition of the Lick Observatory. The star images are too small to be seen, but circles marked around them show where they are. By comparing this plate with one of the same section of the sky taken on some earlier night a minute displacement of the star images away from the sun could be detected on the eclipse plate. This indicates that a ray of starlight passing close to the sun is bent toward the sun as predicted by Einstein.

Aside from its interest in relation to the Einstein theory this plate shows a fine picture of the corona, the mysterious luminous rays that extend out into space for millions of miles. They are now thought to consist of minute particles of matter driven out from the solar atmosphere by the pressure of the light. The corona varies greatly in extent and form as seen in successive eclipses.

Suppose some erratic oak-tree, in a desire to be original, should begin to bear watermelons instead of acorns? Who is entitled to say it that it cannot? Suppose the earth should get tired of always turning the same way and take a notion to turn from east to west for a change? How do you know it won't? You don't know. Yet you are sure it won't.

The only reason you can give is that this never has happened, but that is merely the prejudice of the conservative, the negation of all progress.

Yet this principle, that like causes always produce like effects, has to be assumed by pure faith before we can undertake our next day's work. It is also a necessary assumption in all scientific calculations. Let us consider, for instance, the astronomer, for he indulges in longer-term prophecies with greater assurance and success than any other scientist. The point is best put by a French poet, Sully-Prudhomme, in a beautiful sonnet that may be translated as follows:

THE RENDEZVOUS [1]

'T is late; the astronomer his vigil stern
On lofty tower prolongs. In silent space
He seeks his golden isles, nor turns his face
Till the starry host grows pale with morn's return.
Bright worlds, as grain the winnowing flail doth spurn,
Fly past thick-clustering nebulæ a-light;
His eager gaze one streaming orb pursues in flight.
He calls: "This hour, ten centuries hence, return."
Return it shall. Nor time nor space abates,
The Everlasting Fact it never can assail.

[1] Translated by F. P. H.

Men pass from view; Eternal Science waits.
And though Humanity itself should fail,
Fair Truth will stand, alone, upon the tower
To keep that tryst at the appointed hour.

Now, I fancy that Sully-Prudhomme with poetic license has exaggerated a bit the marvelous power of prescience possessed by the astronomer. To fix the exact hour for a comet's return a thousand years in advance is rather closer figuring than we can do with certainty. There is always the possibility that the comet may be wrecked in a collision or side-tracked by some star.

But Sully-Prudhomme does not exaggerate the confidence of the scientist in his fundamental principle of the constancy of natural law. The astronomer is willing to stake his life, or what he values more, his scientific reputation, that if none of these accidents happen and if he has rightly weighed all the factors involved, the result will be exactly as he says. He is so sure of it that if a comet does not return on an expected date he will be confident that some unforeseen force has intervened and he will set about to find it. If he does not find out what is wrong, other astronomers will take up the task and devote their lives to finding the cause of the discrepancy. They may keep at the problem for a thousand years and never think of saying: "Well, perhaps there isn't any reason. Comets are queer things, anyway."

And if an oak-tree should take to bearing watermelons—things almost as unexpected have happened— the botanists would be absolutely positive there was something new inside or outside the tree that set it to acting so. They would begin experimenting and probably find out what it was in the course of time. "There's a reason," is the faith of the scientist, and so far he has never been belied.

68

TERRITORIAL WARS OF BIRDS

The desire for exclusive possession of land, which according to the conservatives is the foundation of civilization and according to the radicals is the root of all evil, is commonly supposed to be a purely human instinct. But it seems that this virtue or vice is shared by the birds. When you see two birds fighting, the chances are that it is not a romantic duel over some fascinating lady bird but a sordid dispute over land limits. When you see an early bird in the springtime perched upon a tree-top and singing lustily you may reasonably infer that he has taken that prominent position so that he can keep a wary eye out for poachers while he signals to his mate to come and help him hold the fort.

"Birds of a feather flock together"—until the time comes for them to settle down. Then they "flock separately," as Lord Dunsany—no, I mean *Lord Dundreary*—used to say. In the spring a young bird's fancy lightly turns to thoughts of love. But his impulse leads him in a direction opposite to what one might expect. Instead of seeking the society of the other sex, he turns his back upon it and sets out alone or with other bachelor birds in search of a homestead. With more foresight than most young men, he will not seek a mate until he has a home to offer her equal to the one she was brought up in.

When he finds a suitable locality he preëmpts a claim or jumps one and then stays on the spot ready to defend it against all comers. Meanwhile he puts in his time sitting and singing on some conspicuous post in the midst of his homestead. The song may sound to us like a careless carol, the involuntary outpouring of a mirthful heart. But actually it is a piteous appeal for a partner, for a helpmate who can make a home on the claim he has taken up. I have found the same sentiment in old letters written by a young pioneer from a homestead in the Far West to the girl he left behind him down east.

A week or ten days later the female birds begin to arrive and pick out promising mates who sing engagingly and have shown good judgment in the selection of a home-site. As the pair settle down and get at nest building, a fierce proprietary instinct takes possession of them. The birds then cease to be sociable and gregarious and migratory. They become sedentary and jealous and pugnacious. They recant their communism and become peasant proprietors, each attached to his bit of soil and intolerant of all trespassers. Any attempt to jump the claim or even to search for food on this plot of ground by birds of the same species or another is quickly resented and leads to border conflicts. Both sexes take part in the fighting, male against male, female against female, or one pair against another pair in a mixed foursome.

A series of such frontier fights settles the boundary-line as definitely as if the land had been surveyed into sections and quarter-sections and the limits marked by fences or terminal stones. Eliot Howard, who has been watching the finches, warblers, and other birds of England at close range for twenty years, gives in his book on "Territory in Bird Life," maps of a meadow in which lapwings have settled for successive years. They look like the map of a mining-camp. Each family has an acre or two of its own in the form of a square or triangle or irregular polygon, and then there is a patch of neutral ground where all the birds feed in amity without claiming any exclusive territorial rights. For the sea-birds suitable nesting-grounds in the cliffs are restricted so that each family can hold but a few square feet and the plots must be defined by inches like a city building lot. Consequently the "land wars" are fierce and frequent here. But those species which agree easily to a compromise that gives them undisputed possession of a fair and reasonable allotment of the land will prosper more than those species that waste several weeks of precious springtime quarreling about it. The phrase "survival of the fittest" cannot then be misinterpreted as the "survival of the fightest." On the contrary, the establishment of a system of title guarantee and mutual respect for property rights among the feathered bipeds contributes to survival value in the struggle for existence. The answer to the old conundrum, "Why do little birds in their nest agree?" —"Because if they did not they would fall out"—has a sociological significance.

Mr. Howard thinks that Darwin was wrong in assuming that bird fights are between males for the possession of a particular female. He finds that both sexes often take part in such conflicts and that the cause of the quarrel is more commonly land than love. In this hitherto neglected factor of territorial claims he discovers a hidden motive of migration and an important cause of evolution.

This theory makes the birds seem more human than ever. But in one significant respect they differ decidedly from featherless bipeds. They never fight for more land than they need.

69

FARADAY'S RAZORS

An unpublished letter which Principal J. C. Irvine brought to the attention of the British Association at Hull shows how slow industry has been in recognizing the value of scientific research. Michael Faraday had in the course of his investigations at the Royal Institution in London discovered a new process and of course made it public without ever trying to make money out of it. But a manufacturer, who had adopted the process and used it in business and to his profit, was not entirely ungrateful. Faraday in a letter to a friend says:

He writes me word that having repeated our experiments, he finds the product very good, and as our information was given openly to the world he, as a matter of compliment, has presented me with some pairs of razors to give away.

You will see that Faraday, while pleased with the "compliment," did not even think of keeping a razor for himself.

That was a hundred years ago. Nowadays steel manufacturers know the value of chemists better and often employ them on salaries not much smaller than are paid to union laborers. Chemists also know their own value better, and once in a while one of them is able to make a fortune for himself out of his discoveries. But still the industries do not pay much more in proportion to the sciences from which they derive their ideas than did that old British razor-maker to Faraday.

If Faraday had been a shrewd financier instead of a simple-minded scientist and if he had been able to get, say, one per cent of the value that his discoveries have given to the world he, or rather his heirs, would now be richer than any man alive. For it is to Faraday that we owe the primary idea of the dynamo, the electric motor, the liquefaction of gases, the decomposition of salts by the electric current, and the theory of magnetism.

If Faraday had "kept an eye on the main chance" he would not have done so much for science, and it was much better that his researches should have been "given openly to the world" rather than patented for his own profit or somebody else's.

But the cutlery maker should not have felt the debt handsomely repaid by the gift of "some pairs of razors." He and other manufacturers who made money out of his ideas should have paid part of their gains to the Royal Institution.   Then the Royal Institution could have paid Faraday and other poor boys more than the five hundred dollars a year he received.

But the question of how to make industry pay its honest debt to research and how to make a man of science active without making him avaricious and to keep him sufficiently well fed without making him fat and lazy is a question not yet solved.

70

BACK OF BABEL

The premature attempt to construct a sky-scraper in Babylon some five thousand years ago was stopped by the curse of the confusion of tongues. When the mason at the top of the tower yelled down, "More mort!"— meaning by that a bucket of bitumen—the hod-carrier was as likely as not to tote up to him a tale of adobe bricks. This caused hard feelings and harsh language.

The curse of the confusion of tongues has rested upon the world ever since. It is getting worse of late. The Great War brought to birth a dozen new nations, which are now struggling to survive the diseases of infancy. These new nations are bursting with patriotism, and their self-respect demands that their vernacular shall be placed on a parity with the leading languages of the world. Every country is ambitious to attain economic and cultural independence and is striving for it by tariff walls, postal impediments, embargos, and boycotts. Nationalism is the order of the day. Secession and separation are in the air. The new map of Europe looks like a patchwork crazy-quilt. The map-maker can hardly muster up enough different colors to keep the countries distinct.

But while statesmen are breaking up the world into smaller portions scientists are bringing the world together. Paint up the map into as many patches as you please, but it is impossible to put up partitions in the ether. Wireless waves know no nationality. They spread in all directions equally, and nothing can keep them out. The frontier may be lined with custom-house officers, censors, and soldiers, but the radio-waves will pass right through them. Anybody anywhere may listen in without the consent or knowledge of the sender. Walls and mountains, rivers and seas, do not prevent the passage of the ether messages.

But there is something that acts as an absolute barrier. This is difference of language. The curse of Babel rests upon the radio. What if the telephone of the Eiffel Tower in Paris can reach all Europe and North Africa if the peoples within hearing talk thirty diverse languages?

So long as most people lived all their lives in one place it did not matter if every valley spoke a divergent tongue. So long as intercommunication was confined to print, mail, and telegraph, it was possible to get along with the aid of interpreters, but when millions are receiving messages without intermediaries they must have a common language.

A few years ago it was an open question whether we ever could or would have a common language. To-day it is not a question of could or would; it is a matter of must.

We 've got to have one.

The only question now is what the international language shall be. And how we shall get it.

Already under the pressure of necessity various international languages are growing up. The commercial and maritime codes of the world comprise a larger vocabulary than many historic tongues. Music and mathematics have a common symbolism the world over. The names and formulas of the sciences are much the same in all languages. Possibly these separate and spontaneous movements may grow eventually into some sort of a world language, but it would be a very haphazard and unsatisfactory affair.

Five hundred years ago Europe had an international language. Latin was spoken and read by the learned classes of all lands. Some professors now propose to revive Latin as the common language of commerce, diplomacy, and science. But its advocates are divided into three classes. Some want the Latin that Cicero wrote restored in all its purity. Some will accept the forms developed by medieval schools and churchmen. Some say that Latin will stand no chance of adoption by the modern world until it is simplified by being freed of its irregularities and cumbrous conjugations.

It would seem sensible to adopt some living language. But which? If we should put it to a popular vote Chinese would win by a large plurality. But who can learn the Chinese alphabet? It has n't any. Shall the world be asked to accept Russian with its unpronounceable consonants, German with its unspeakable grammar, English with its illogical spelling, or French with its elusive idioms? Mutual jealousy will probably prevent

the people of the earth from agreeing to adopt any of
the existing tongues as a medium of international
communication.

Finally, there are several languages invented for the
express purpose; nice tidy tongues; no exceptions to
the rules, no irregular verbs; pronounced as spelled and
spelled as pronounced; said to be easy to learn—but not
enough people are learning them. Here, too, there is
rivalry. Esperanto is now in the lead, but Ido claims
to be an improvement on it.

In some way or other the world will soon acquire
a common medium of communication. The more numerous the languages the more need for another that all
peoples shall know. So the forces of nationalism will
force internationalism. We must somehow get back of
Babel; back to those paradisial days when all the earth
had one speech.

71

HOME-MADE RUBBER

It is to be hoped that part of the half-million dollars
that Congress has recently appropriated for developing
a domestic rubber supply will be devoted to investi-
gating the possibilities of home-made, as well as of
home-grown, rubber. It is all right to start rubber
plantations in the Philippines. If we had done that
ten years ago we should not now be at the mercy of
the British rubber-growers. Let us also milk the milk-
weed if it can be induced to give down. But let us

further give the chemist a chance to see what he can do in the way of competing with the agriculturist. He has beaten him on madder and indigo. Perhaps he can do it on caout-chouc.

We know that rubber can be made in the laboratory. At the International Congress of Applied Chemistry held in New York shortly before the war the German chemist Duisberg proudly exhibited in the Great Hall of the College of the City of New York a pair of tires that had been made from synthetic rubber and had run an automobile a thousand miles or more. The British chemist, Sir William Perkin, promptly countered with a different process for making artificial rubber. Neither process has so far proved a commercial success, but the chemists have not given up the problem.

In 1922 Plotnikoff announced in a German periodical that caout-chouc chloride could be readily made by the action of ultra-violet rays on vinyl chloride. Now, the caout-chouc chloride can be easily converted into ordinary rubber, and vinyl chloride can be made from acetylene, which, as every automobilist knows or used to know, can be made by dropping calcium carbide into water, and calcium carbide can be made from coal and lime by the electrical furnace, and the electrical power can be got from waterfalls.

But where can we get the ultra-violet rays? There are plenty in the sunshine, but they are pretty well filtered out by the atmosphere before it gets to us, luckily, for otherwise we would get worse sunburned than we do. Various forms of mercury-vapor and arc-lamps will give off ultra-violet rays, but that is too expensive.

Now, the ultra-violet rays differ from the rays that we can see only in having shorter wave-lengths. Sometimes we see a tall man walking with his short wife, both at the same gait but she taking two steps to his one. So all kinds of light travel with the same speed in empty space, but the violet takes two steps to the red's one; and the rays beyond, that is, the ultra-violet, step faster still.

But a polite man will shorten his pace to accommodate the lady he is walking with, even if she is his wife. Cannot light of long wave-length be induced somehow to shorten its wave? In other words, cannot ordinary sunshine be converted into ultra-violet light, or at any rate be made to act the same? It can in various ways, and Plotnikoff has shown that if a salt of uranium is added sunlight will serve as well as ultra-violet in effecting the transformation to rubber.

There is nothing absurd about making rubber with sunlight. All the rubber we use is made that way. And if a tree can use sunshine for that purpose why cannot the chemist? We have plenty of sunshine, more than most countries, and more than we want in summer. If there can be devised satisfactory step-up transformers to change sunshine into ultra-violet rays we might make not only rubber but a host of other things for which we now depend on plants, and we could use this energetic agent for speeding up numerous chemical manufactures.

72

SCIENCE GIVES BEFORE SHE IS ASKED

What is commonly called applied science is often nothing of the sort. It may be the uncomprehended discovery of some unscientific inventor, unknown workman, or untutored savage. Years after it has been in use comes the scientist who discloses the reason of it and claims it as an application of his new principle. But times are changing, and now the scientist leads the technologist in many lines.

The compass had been known for some forty-five hundred years before Faraday showed the relation between electricity and magnetism in 1821. This not merely explained the mystery of the magnetic needle, but it led to the dynamo and all its innumerable applications. The chemist cannot claim vegetable indigo, since its use dates from undated times. But he can claim synthetic indigo and all the host of dyes that came from aniline. The wild wheat of Palestine was the gift of nature. The rustless wheat of Manitoba is the creation of the plant-breeder.

I am dwelling upon these familiar facts because it does not seem to me to be sufficiently realized that we are entering upon a new era when science shall devise and direct and not merely interpret. This is the era which Francis Bacon foretold three hundred years ago when he said in "De Dignitate et Augmentis Scientiarum":

As a man may proceed on his path in three ways: he may grope his way for himself in the dark; he may be led by the hand of another, without himself seeing anything; or lastly, he may get a light and so direct his steps; in like manner when a man tries all kinds of experiments without order or method, this is but groping in the dark, but when he gets some direction and order in experimenting, it is as if he were led by the hand, and this is what I mean by Learned Experience. For the light itself, which was the third way, is to be sought from the Interpretation of Nature, or the Organon.

We have now passed, in several of the sciences, from groping in the dark or being led step by step, to the Era of Enlightment where we can survey the whole field in front of us and choose the straightest path to our goal.

Nowadays discoveries do not always "fill a long-felt want," to use the familiar phrase. The want has often to be created after the discovery is made, usually with the aid of the advertiser. The unimaginative masses do not ask for comforts and conveniences that they have never known or dreamed of. It was no great popular demand that created the phonograph and the motion-picture, yet nothing is more popular.

Formerly a manufacturer who felt the need of some new material, say a dye-stuff or a dielectric, was forced to survey the world from China to Peru in search of it. Now he sits in his office and has offered to him all sorts of new substances in the hope that he will grant them the favor of a try-out. A physician may have more new remedies sent to him as samples than he has patients to use them on. This is the way it should be, for with science in the lead mankind will make more rapid progress.

73

THE SCHOLAR IN OVERALLS

The present age is sharply distinguished from all that preceded it in the history of the human race by the amazing increase in wealth. In every civilized country the value of property per capita is far greater than ever before, notwithstanding the unprecedented increase in population during the last century and the rise of living expenses among all classes. Luxuries longed for or undreamed of by our parents are our common household conveniences. Our tenements are better than medieval palaces. Financial magnates employ corps of experts in the art of high living for the purpose of inventing new ways of spending more money and persuading people to adopt them. The bitter attack now being made from all sides against our unequal and inequitable method of distribution is due to the fact that there is more wealth to distribute than ever before. The bigger the spoil the more strenuous the struggle. The bricklayers now get more than professors used to, and still they are not satisfied; and there is no reason why they should be so long as they can get more.

This sudden increase in the wealth of the world can be traced to one cause. There is a new factor in civilization. This new wealth is the gift of modern applied science. All the other wealth-producing factors have remained substantially unaltered. The natural resources of the earth are no greater; in fact, they are less, for our soil is less fertile and our ore lies deeper. It is not the discovery of America, adding two continents of new land, that has brought about this increased prosperity, for the most densely populated countries in Europe were increasing in wealth almost as rapidly as we were until they took to wasting it in war. The Old World has always had waste land enough. Already Americans are emigrating to Africa and Asia. It is not because men of ability are any more common than they used to be. There has been no sudden eruption of genius on this planet. There has been no perceptible improvement in the human race since the time of Aristotle, either in the intelligence of the average man or in the number or eminence of the exceptional men.

Our enhanced wealth is not the product of manual labor. Men have always worked hard enough; never harder probably than when the fellaheen built the pyramids of Egypt. There have always been capitalists, too, not so numerous nor so rich as at the present time, but enough to carry out large industrial enterprises whose ruins astonish us yet. Wars are not so frequent as they used to be, but they are more destructive, and Europe never spent so much in the most belligerent crises of past centuries as is now spent continuously on armies and navies in this so-called period of peace following the Great War.

No, what we have that our ancestors had not is more knowledge of the laws of nature and more willingness to apply them. There are some who complain that science is becoming commercialized. That may be, but a commercialized science makes greater progress than a philosophized science ever did, greater progress even in its most abstract branches. The shop is pushing the study. The mathematician works as he always has for the pure joy of seeing what the human mind can do with lines and numbers and quantities; but now the engineer waits impatiently beside his desk, like the office-boy on the editor, to take his formulas from him before the ink is dry to construct a new dynamo with them. The chemist, working with the electric furnace out of pure curiosity and the desire to read a paper before the academy, makes some new carbides; within a few years the waterfalls of Europe and America are making them by the ton, and the automobiles are lighted by acetylene and polished with carborundum. A new element is discovered, good for nothing apparently except to fill a gap in Mendeléef's table, but it speedily appears in our gas-burners and cuts down our bills.

It is this middleman between the scientist and the mechanic who is the new force which is accelerating the wheels of progress. It is the engineer, the technician; his profession is so recent that it has no proper name, but it has already made good its claim to an equal place beside the three historic learned professions. It requires no less scholarly preparation; in fact, it is cheaper to educate a lawyer or a minister, if not a doctor, than a technologist, and the last has greater assurance of immediate paying employment and better prospects for rising to a position of affluence. Some of our great industrial establishments have a standing offer of a job for all graduates of certain schools of technology. They tempt seniors to desert their class-work and even fish for likely juniors, "rushing" them and getting them pledged in advance as college students work for their fraternities and athletic teams.

Science is a new exponent that raises the efficiency of the individual to a higher power, but we do not know its limiting value. One man now makes twice as many tons of iron as he did a few years ago. In some manufactories, where twenty or fifty men formerly were condemned to hard labor for life, now there are two or three, and they have little to do but watch dials and press buttons. We are told that the capitalist is destroying the middle class. It is still more significant of modern tendencies that the technician is eliminating the working class. In most industries the number of workmen is diminishing in ratio to the amount of the product. The future will have little use for the physical strength of man. Labor-saving and wealth-producing inventions will in time give the political economists something worth talking about.

74

Furfural Wants a Job

A new material has come into the market and wants to make itself useful if any one can show it how. Its name is "furfural"; queer sounding, but not so hard to pronounce as most chemical terms. The public is lucky to be let off with only three syllables and those slipping easily off the tongue.

Two years ago furfural was selling at thirty dollars a pound. Or rather this was the price it was quoted at in lists of rare chemicals. Really it was not selling at all, except when a professor wanted a little vial of it to put into his museum case of organic preparations.

But it is now known that the stuff can be made cheaply from materials that are still going to waste in unlimited amounts, such as corn-cobs, oat-hulls, straw, and the like. Consequently, furfural is now quoted at twenty-five cents a pound and could be made very much cheaper, perhaps six cents a pound in a large-scale plant, one capable of taking in, say, a hundred tons of cobs a day and turning out nine tons of furfural. All that is needed is to cook up the cobs with steam.

I saw it done at the color laboratory of the Department of Agriculture, on the Arlington Farm, just across the Potomac River from Washington. A large steel still was set up in the center of the big building. Two bags of corn-cobs were dumped into the cylinder; then the top was screwed on and the steam turned in. After digesting for a couple of hours the furfural was distilled in a stream of steam, and the water and furfural condensed together by cooling. This mixture is afterward separated by redistillation.

Furfural is a liquid, clear and colorless as water when fresh and pure, but turning brown when exposed to light and air. It takes fire easily and burns with a bright flame. It has a characteristic odor, but not

EXPERIMENTAL FURFURAL PLANT OF THE COLOR LABORATORY,
BUREAU OF CHEMISTRY, DEPARTMENT OF AGRICULTURE,
ARLINGTON, VA.

In the background is the tall steel cylinder in which the corn cobs are
digested. In the foreground is the apparatus in which the distillate
from the digester is redistilled and the furfural separated out.

strong or unpleasant. It is what the chemist calls a "ring compound," for its molecule is composed of four atoms of carbon and one of oxygen, connected in a ring, with an extra atom of carbon and another of oxygen and four hydrogen atoms attached outside.

But we are all more interested in what furfural can do than in what it is. This, however, remains to be found out. The first thing that we think of is using it as a motor fuel, since a shortage of gasolene is impending. Furfural can run a car but does not seem to be suited to the ordinary type of motor, and anyhow it is about twice as high as gasolene and therefore out of reach.

Furfural is poisonous to insects and germs. Perhaps it could find employment here. It will dissolve paint and varnish; also fats and airplane dope.

More promising yet are its compounds. Furfural will combine with various coal-tar products such as aniline and carbolic acid. With aniline and the like, it makes dyes of a variety of colors, but those so far made are fugitive.

With carbolic acid, furfural combines to form resins very much like bakelite, which is made from carbolic acid and formalin. These may be used in liquid form for varnishes or in solid form as insulation in electrical apparatus. We may expect furfural some day to appear in disguise as amber beads or tortoise-shell combs or ivory billiard-balls or horn buttons. Phonograph records may be made from it, also plates for printing from instead of type. They are light, hard and tough.

In short, furfural is now in the position of a high-school graduate whom the principal claps on the shoulder and says: "You are a bright, versatile fellow. There is a great future before you." But when the boy asks, "Where?" he gets no answer.

This new-comer is knocking at the factory door with no credentials but a letter of introduction from the chemist, which does not go far in the factory. The busy manufacturer turns to him long enough to ask: "Can you do anything better than those I've got, or do it cheaper?" The applicant can only answer: "I don't know, sir. I think so, but I've never had a chance to show what I can do yet. Won't you give me a try-out?"

I can't give the answer of the business man, because I don't know what it is.

75

Coal-Oil from Coal

When kerosene first came into use as a lamp illuminant it was called "coal-oil," for it used to be supposed that petroleum had somehow been formed from coal. Later that theory was called in question, and geologists are still disputing the origin of oil. We seem likely to use it up before we find out where it came from. But even if coal-oil turns out to have been an inappropriate name in the past, it may prove to be true in the future. For petroleum can be made from coal, and some day we may have to make it that way.

For the less oil we have the more we use. The lower the supply in the ground the higher the output of our

refineries. According to the report of the Bureau of
Mines for January, 1923, twenty million gallons of gasolene were turned out every day during that month on
the average, while for the same month in 1922 the output
was fourteen million gallons. This increase cannot keep
up forever, however liberally you may estimate our
unseen supply underground.

The countries that are short on petroleum are already
contriving substitutes. The Germans, who were well
supplied with coal but had little oil, began before the
war experimenting on methods of making artificial
petroleum. Since they have lost some of their best coal-
fields through the war and oil is harder to get than ever,
they have been still more active in such research, and
it is rumored by returned travelers that they have been
more successful in that quest than has appeared in
print. What little has leaked out has mostly come
through the patents which Friedrich Bergius has taken
out in Germany and the United States from 1914 to
1922. But a patent, especially a German patent, is by
no means so ''patent'' as it is supposed to be; so not
much is known by the outside world about the details
or the practicability of the process.

Theoretically it is simple enough. Petroleum is a
mixture of compounds of hydrogen and carbon. Just
hitch up these two elements, and there you are!

But there are other hitches in the proceedings. Either
carbon and hydrogen will unite readily with oxygen,
but they have little liking for each other. Only when
stirred up by high heat and forced into contact by high
pressure will they combine. Besides the expense of
the process, there is the expense of the materials. Car-

bon is cheap and abundant enough in the form of coal, but hydrogen has to be obtained by tearing it away from the oxygen with which it is combined in water. This may be done by passing steam over red-hot iron turnings, which pick up the oxygen and release the hydrogen. Or steam may be passed through beds of hot coal, which gives what is known as "water-gas," a mixture of hydrogen and carbon monoxide, both good combustibles.

In making synthetic petroleum it appears that the coal is first powdered and mixed with heavy oils. This pasty mess is put into a tight steel retort, and a current of hydrogen or water-gas is run through the vessel at a temperature of about seven hundred degrees Fahrenheit and a pressure of a hundred atmospheres.

Under these conditions the carbon and the hydrogen gas unite in all sorts of ways and form liquid products, and an oil much like natural petroleum distils off from the retort. This is redistilled; the lighter fractions are collected as gasolene, kerosene, benzene, and the like; and the heavy residue is returned to the retort mixed with the next batch of coal.

It is asserted that by such a process as high as eighty-seven per cent of the carbon in the coal can be converted into liquid hydrocarbons, such as are found in natural petroleum, and also into the coal-tar products which can be used as material for dyes and drugs, preservatives and perfumes. The nitrogen in the coal, which is lost in ordinary combustion, is here obtained in the valuable form of ammonia.

The coal for this process does not have to be of a special quality as is required in making gas or coke by our present methods. Any kind or form of coal can be used, and high yields of the hydrogenated products are said to be obtained from the brown coal and lignite of which Germany has an abundance. Peat may be thus worked up into gasolene and other marketable compounds—also pitch, tar, sawdust, and any vegetable material.

Although there is little likelihood at present that such a complicated process will come into use here so long as our oil-wells continue to flow, it is reassuring to know that when they do run out we shall not be altogether deprived of the efficient fuel that has made the automobile, the airplane and the motor-boat possible. We would not know how to get along without the paraffin, vaseline, lubricating-oil, and innumerable other petroleum products that enter into our daily life. Mineral oil contains so many such valuable substances that it is a pity to burn it up in running steam-engines where other fuels may serve. As petroleum gets scarcer, we may expect to see the burning of the crude oil prohibited.

76

A New Path to Oblivion

It is within the memory of many still living that science revealed to mankind means of escape from the pains of disease and surgery. Nitrous oxide and ether were used for amusement long before they were used for relief. Medical students in New England used to take laughing-gas or indulged in "ether frolics" for the fun of the thing without thinking of the possibilities of applying it in their profession.

But in 1844 a Connecticut chemist named Colton had a big back tooth pulled out after inhaling nitrous oxide, and two years later Dr. Morton, a Boston dentist, put himself to sleep with ether and then tried it on a patient who came into his office as he awoke. The use of anesthetics was bitterly opposed at first on the ground that pain was a punishment or a natural process and that it was cowardly or wicked to evade it, but the new practice prevailed and has brought surcease of suffering to uncountable millions of men, women, and children in the last seventy-five years.

Nitrous oxide and ether have been the chief means of producing complete unconsciousness, but now a new agent of anesthesia has entered the field that promises to rival or supplant both. This is ethylene, a gas composed of hydrogen and carbon, long in use for illuminating but which has recently been found by Professor A. B. Luckhardt of the University of Chicago to have the power of putting a person to sleep without the danger and unpleasant after-effects that sometimes attend the use of the older anesthetics. On inhaling the gas the patient passes quickly into insensibility and then into complete unconsciousness. The respiration and blood-pressure remain regular, and the muscles are relaxed. The recovery is remarkably rapid. Within three or five minutes the patient comes to his senses and usually without nausea. In the case of a severe operation on the leg the patient had to be kept under the influence for three hours and ten minutes continuously.

Yet five minutes afterward he had become conscious, got off the operating-table himself, and two hours later ate a meal.

The new anesthetic was first used at the Presbyterian Hospital in Chicago, where operations of all sorts were successfully performed under its influence. A Chicago dentist extracted teeth using ethylene in place of nitrous oxide, and it has also been found useful in normal childbirth.

The discovery of the soporific effect of ethylene came through a curious chain of circumstances. In 1908 the carnation-growers complained that they were losing money because the flowers they shipped to Chicago went to sleep when put in the greenhouses and the buds failed to open. A couple of botanists from the University of Chicago were assigned to the job of running down the reason of this floral ''sleeping-sickness'' and found that it was due to the leakage of illuminating-gas, which contained four per cent of ethylene. This is commonly added to city gas to increase its candle-power. Plants are extremely susceptible to ethylene. Sweet peas will droop their leaves if the room contains one part of ethylene in a million of the air, a much more delicate test for its presence than any chemical reaction. This may be a reason why plants do not thrive and people get sleepy in houses where the gas-fixtures are leaky.

Since the investigation now led out of the vegetable kingdom and into the animal, it passed over into the hands of the physiologists, who carried the experiments on up the scale of life, using frogs, mice, rats, guinea-pigs, rabbits, kittens, and dogs successively as subjects.

It was found that ethylene brought the animals into unconsciousness in half or a quarter of the time necessary for nitrous oxide and that they recovered more quickly.

Finally Dr. Luckhardt and his colleague, Mr. Carter, having thus assured themselves of its safety and learned how to administer it, tried it on themselves and for several successive Sunday afternoons put themselves to sleep by the inhalation of ethylene.

The gas is inhaled with oxygen as is the custom with nitrous oxide. Between eighty and ninety per cent of ethylene is sufficient in most cases to bring the patient to the point where a surgical operation may be carried on. Care must be taken, of course, to see that the gas is pure and also to keep it away from flames, since ethylene, like ether vapor, is inflammable.

The brief history of ethylene as an anesthetic is a striking illustration of the acceleration of scientific progress in this century. In 1798 Humphry Davy, then only twenty-two, discovered nitrous oxide and suggested that it might be used to stop the pain of surgery, but it was half a century before this hint was acted upon— fifty years of unnecessary pain and loss of life. But in the case of ethylene the progress from pinks and peas to professors and patients was made with swift, sure steps and in the course of a few months humanity was receiving relief from this new source.

When it was proposed to erect in Boston a monument to the discoverer of anesthesia a hot discussion took place as to who was entitled to the honor. Should it be Dr. Morton, who pulled the first tooth with ether, or Dr. Jackson, who told him how to use it? Dr. Oliver

Wendell Holmes then suggested that the statues of both claimants be put on one pedestal, which should be inscribed "To Ether." This is one of the jokes that no Englishman can understand, for he would pronounce it "eye-ther."

If ethylene proves to be as useful as it seems to be, room must be found on the same pedestal for Dr. Luckhardt, even though it spoil the pun.

77

MEDIUMS AND TRICKSTERS

Those who believe in spiritistic phenomena call upon their opponents to disprove their hypothesis, and hold, rightly enough, that if ninety-nine mediums are merely tricksters, it does not prove that the hundredth is not genuine. It is, of course, impossible to prove the universal negative of such a proposition. It is merely a question of probabilities. We can merely say that if spirits do return, it is extremely unfortunate that they can only return under those conditions which are most favorable for deception.

What these conditions are we can learn from the practices of amateur and professional conjurers. Let us approach the matter from another starting-point than is usually adopted. Instead of speculating as to how departed spirits would manifest themselves to us, a matter which we can know nothing about, let us consider what a trickster would do if he wished to deceive the public into thinking that he was possessed of spirit power, a matter on which we have unfortunately a great deal of information. What conditions would he impose? What methods would he use? The following are the chief characteristics of such fraudulent manifestations:

(1) Darkness. The less the light the more remarkable the manifestations is the general rule.

(2) Distraction of attention. This is the chief reliance of the parlor medium and of the stage magician. The most striking things in the séance-room occur after the sitters are tired of watching.

(3) Unexpectedness. An experimenter lets us know what effect he is trying to get, and even if the experiment does not work he does not palm off some entirely different phenomenon and assert that he has succeeded. The feats of the conjurer—and of the medium—are capricious and unforeseen. That is why trickery cannot be guarded against by precautions in advance.

(4) Control of conditions. The conjurer and the mediums alike insist on having lights, furniture, sitters, and apparatus arranged to suit themselves. On the other hand, the primary requisite of an experiment is the control of conditions. It is, therefore, incorrect to speak of experiments with mediums. They are usually merely observations, and that under circumstances most unfavorable to correct observation.

(5) Suggestion. This is the main reliance of the magician, next to distraction of attention. He palms a coin while pretending to throw it into a hat or into the air. Our eyes follow the motion of his hand and interpret it according to the intent. It is easy under favorable circumstances to cause collective hallucinations of smell, sight, or sound. Our sense of hearing is

particularly likely to be deceived as to the character and direction of a sound, such as the raps and scratches which are the commonest of mediumistic phenomena.

(6) Concealment. A prestidigitator for his most difficult tricks requires some kind of a table, shelf, or screen, but he rarely demands so convenient a shelter as the medium's cabinet or curtain.

(7) Tied or held hands. The releasing of hands and feet when they are bound, knotted, and sealed is the cheapest of tricks. I have seen a man handcuffed by a policeman, tied in a bag, and thrown into the river, yet he came to the surface promptly with his hands free.

(8) Involuntary assistance. The respectable and well-meaning gentlemen whom the audience select to represent them on the stage do not interfere with the magician. On the contrary, they often aid as well as give him countenance. The magnetic girl who used to throw strong men about the stage was really utilizing their strength, not her own. Where several persons have their hands on a table it is impossible to prevent their taking an active part in its motion.

(9) Emotional excitement. An experimenter must preserve a cool and somewhat detached demeanor. Now, even the most convinced skeptic cannot witness unmoved such violations of natural law as these, purporting to prove the existence of another world, and especially the presence of his deceased friends and relatives. The photographs taken of the séance-room show us not merely that the table is suspended in mid-air, but that the witnesses, watching it with bulging eyes, open mouths, and strained attention, are incapable of critical observation.

In these nine points and others the conditions of successful trickery and the conditions of the séance are the same. For that reason and others most scientists do not think it worth while to spend their time on spiritualism.

We do not yet know how to explain all these mysterious doings, and we do not yet know whether there is anything here that requires explanation. There are to-day, as there always have been, thousands of persons claiming to possess supernatural powers, but not one of them can demonstrate it by any kind of experiment that can be repeated and verified. A scientist who, in the physical, chemical, biological, or even the psychological laboratory, discovers a new force or effect, no matter how delicate or under what complicated conditions, has no difficulty in promptly proving its existence to the satisfaction of everybody, but the forces which are said to pervade the séance-room are supposed to be strong enough to lift a table or a person, and they are sufficiently at command to be produced whenever anybody is willing to pay for them, yet they remain as unpredictable, unrepeatable, and elusive as ever.

78

Tangling Up the Time Line

Einstein's theory of relativity is like a magician's bag. There seems to be no end to the queer things that can be pulled out of it. The more it is studied the more paradoxical it appears.

The latest thing I have seen is the queerest, the idea that the future may get tangled up in the present or even in the past. It is all worked out mathematically in a book now translated from the German, Weyl's "Time—Space—Matter." [1] Too mathematical for most of us but the point in plain language is this:

Here is a line representing the course of time extending from the dim past into the indefinite future:

Past	I	Future

The present is the point where I stand, looking both ways like Janus, but not seeing any end in either direction. I am continually moving or being moved straight along the time road from left to right. Every instant I step from the past into the future. Every instant a bit of time is taken from the future and added to the past, though neither gets any smaller or larger, since both are infinite. The past time and the future time are permanently separated by the moving present where I am, and there seems no chance of the two kinds of time ever getting mixed up, for they extend in opposite directions.

But wait; here's a disconcerting idea. If I roll up the paper I can make the future touch the past. I can overlap them. I can put A.D. into B.C., and what becomes of chronology then?

We are used to this curving of apparently straight lines in space ever since 1492 when men found that they were not living on a flat earth but on a sphere. If I

---

[1] The passage may be also found in "Science," December 29, 1922, where I quoted it in replying to a letter by Dr. W. J. Humphreys in "Science," November 24.

travel straight east from this town I will eventually come back to it from the west. How far I will have to go depends upon where I live. If my home were on the equator, I should have to travel twenty-five thousand miles to get to my starting-point. If it were near one of the poles I could do this astonishing stunt in the course of a morning's walk.

Now, according to Einstein, the time line is like the space lines. The framework of the world is measured by four dimensions, three of space and one of time, namely the up-down, right-left, to-fro, past-future lines. But these are not rigidly fixed. They may be bent and distorted like a bird-cage that has been twisted and crushed, though every wire remains intact and connected to the other wires just the same. Wherever there is a bit of matter, wherever there are electrical or magnetic forces, there the time and space lines are more or less distorted.

If Einstein's theory is accepted by scientists, we shall have to get accustomed to the idea that time—like the tariff—is a local issue; that time measurements like space measurements are relative, not absolute; and that we are not sure of the constancy of our standards of measure in either case. When two things happen in our presence we may be pretty sure which comes first. But if one event is here and another in Mars we cannot be sure about priority with any conceivable system of clocks and signals. What seems past from one standpoint may seem future from another, for the time line may not run straight. Is your present condition in any way the result of your future actions? Can the light of a match be seen before the match is lit? Such a thing is conceivable in the generalized theory of relativity, though, like most other conceivable things, it does not occur, or is never known to occur, in reality. But it is hard to get used to this strange new notion that the future may curl around in some sort of a circle and so come into the past.

Did I say "new"? It was a slip of the pen. For the idea is old. I open a volume of Egyptian antiquities and I see carved on a monument of the Pharaohs, a serpent with its tail in its mouth, the symbol of eternity, of which time is a segment. But what the Egyptians merely guessed at Einstein is putting to the proof.

79

ON TRANSLATING EINSTEIN

Translating mathematics into ordinary language is like translating music. It cannot be done. One could describe in detail a sheet of music and tell the shape of each note and where it is placed on the staff, but that would not convey any idea of how it would sound when played. So, too, I suppose that even the most complicated equation could be described in common words, but it would be so verbose and involved that nobody could get the sense of it. All that can be done is to give by illustrations and analogies some notion of the conception.

This is what I have tried to do in several of these Chats in regard to the Einstein theory of relativity, though well aware that the result is inevitably annoying to the mathematician, who sees the idea distorted without being clarified, and somewhat misleading to the reader, who cannot get in words, either of one syllable or many, the same understanding of it that the mathematician has.

Even—or, rather, especially—where the words used by the mathematician seem familiar is the reader likely to be misled into thinking he understands them. For instance, when he hears the mathematician talk of four, five, or n dimensions he assumes either that the mathematician has supernormal powers of perception or that he is talking nonsense. Neither assumption is justified. The mathematician may be quite an ordinary chap, except for his fondness for x's and y's, and he knows very definitely what he is talking about, though he cannot put it in words.

To those of us who are not professional mathematicians the word "dimension" calls up a more or less clear image of measurement of certain diagrams or models. As a matter of fact, we can only see two dimensions, such as a square or a circle. But we acquire, through painful experience in the early years of our life, a conception of three-dimensional solids, such as a cube or sphere. We can define them by three lines meeting at one point and forming right angles with each other.

But where is the fourth dimension? In what direction does it lie? There is not any room for it in our three-line diagram, no place where it can hitch on to the central point and be at right angles to the other three. We cannot imagine a four-dimensional cube, let alone one of five or six.

But neither can the mathematician, and, what's more, he does not try to. Yet he can tell us how many "sides" and "angles" such a polydimensional solid would have. A "dimension" is to him only a convenient name for a certain algebraic symbol that he finds useful in his calculations, and he can use as many as he likes; his "points," "angles," etc., in polydimensional "spaces" are handy labels for certain types of mathematical expressions, and he does not intend that they shall be taken as referring to physical counterparts similar to those which these words call up in the mind of the average person.

So when Einstein talks about time being the fourth dimension, or about the fourth-dimensional universe being rolled up in the fifth dimension, we need not weary our imaginations trying to form a mental picture of it. Here is simply a case where old words are being stretched to cover a new idea by being used in new, and merely formal, senses. Ideas are born naked and have to be clothed as best we can in hand-me-down language, until new suits can be made for them.

But this should be noted: the Einstein theory is not to be classed with metaphysical speculations of the nature of space and time which have occupied philosophic minds from the time of the Egyptians, Greeks, and Hindus to the present. There is nothing mystical or occult about it. The fourth dimension is not built on to keep spooks in. The theory of relativity is a logical mathematical system of quantitative physical relations which can be definitely proved or disproved wherever means can be found for testing their conformity with natural phenomena. A scientific theory or hypothesis predicts what will happen under certain circumstances. Whether the specified circumstances exist in nature, or can be contrived in the laboratory, remains to be determined by observation. If, when the specified circumstances are found, the predicted result does not follow, the theory is regarded as false and must be rejected or modified. If the specified circumstances cannot be found, then the theory is neither true nor false but merely meaningless.

A scientist works out a theory in much the same way as a tailor makes a suit of clothes. First the tailor makes a few measurements on the man with his tape. Next he cuts out and stitches together the suit. Then he calls in the customer to see if the suit fits in all the places that he did not measure. Usually he finds that he has to do a little stretching or taking in to make it a perfect fit. If it is too bad he has to throw it away and make another out of whole cloth.

So the scientist has to cut his theory to fit the facts, not only the few facts on which he formed his theory but all the facts, including any that will be discovered in the future.

The World has long been wearing the clothing made by the old reliable firm of Galileo, Newton & Co. He was comfortable enough in it, though there were certain points in it which did not quite fit. But a new tailor named Einstein has set up a shop over the way and offers him a new-fashioned suit that he says will fit him perfectly. The World is now wondering whether it is worth while to change when there is so little difference; and then, too, there are some fixings on the new suit that look queer to him.

Or, to drop this plebeian metaphor, the Einstein formulas, fantastic as they seem, work out so nearly the same as the older mechanics in their applications to the physical universe that it is difficult to find any points on which they differ enough to decide between them. In fact only three or four points have been so far suggested in which the difference between the figures given by the two formulas is sufficient to be measured. In these Einstein seems to have the advantage over Newton. Doubtless as the theory is more fully worked out and as new measuring instruments are devised, other ways will be found to test the rival hypotheses.

80

WHICH ORGAN WILL GIVE WAY FIRST

Dr. Oliver Wendell Holmes in his poem on the deacon's one-hoss shay described a vehicle in which the strength of every part was so proportioned to the strain that the whole collapsed together in the end. But the human body is not so evenly constructed, and certain organs, especially the lungs, heart, and kidneys, are likely to show signs of weakness before the others and hence are responsible for a large proportion of the fatalities.

Which is the dangerous point depends upon the age. Professor Raymond Pearl of Johns Hopkins University in collaboration with Chairman Howell has made the most extensive analysis of the causes of death that has yet been undertaken and reported the results before the National Academy of Sciences at its meeting in 1921.

They found that the danger zone during the first year of a child's life is the alimentary canal. Nearly seventy per cent of the male infants and more than forty per cent of the female infants dying under one year of age are victims to some disease of the digestive system.

In the next period of life, which lasts till the fifty-fifth year, the lungs and other parts of the respiratory system are the weak point. The mortality due to diseases of the organs of respiration amounts to more than fifty per cent in infancy and decreases gradually to about twenty-three per cent at the age of fifty-five.

After that age the heart and the circulatory system are most likely to show weakness and to cause death in an increasing proportion of cases.

The lesson of it may be summed up as: In infancy take care of the digestion; in maturity look out for the lungs; in old age watch the heart.

81

The Quantum Theory

You will have to learn about the quantum theory some time, and you might as well do it now as later. It is the latest fad in physics, and it looks as though it had come to stay.

This quantum theory is quite as important and even more disconcerting to ordinary ideas than the relativity theory, but the public has not yet heard so much about it—perhaps because Planck is not so picturesque a personage as Einstein.

The interesting feature of the situation is that physicists have been compelled to go back and pick up an old theory that they had definitely discarded a hundred years before. Newton held the theory that light was due to the emission of minute particles, which moved in straight lines and bounded back like elastic balls from reflecting surfaces. But this could not explain interference, as when two light rays running in the same direction join and produce not double the light but a band of darkness. This could be prettily explained by the theory of Newton's rival, Huyghens of Holland, who held that light was not material but wave-motion of a hypothetical ether; "the nominative of the verb to undulate," as Kelvin called it.

The wave theory served admirably to explain, not only light but also electricity, until recently, when it has been found that light has momentum and exerts a kick when it leaves and a push when it strikes a body, and that there are corpuscles concerned in the interaction of light and electricity.

The crucial experiment between the two theories was the test made by Bennet in 1702 to determine if light exerted any pressure on a body when it struck it as it would if light consisted of minute particles driven straight forward with great velocity. Bennet found no such pressure, and the corpuscular theory was regarded as disproved, although when the wave theory was more fully worked out it was seen that this, too, implied light pressure. As Professor J. J. Thomson says:

It is perhaps fortunate that Bennet had not at his command more delicate apparatus. Had he discovered the pressure of light, it would have shaken confidence in the undulatory theory and checked that magnificent work at the beginning of the last century which so greatly increased our knowledge of optics.

It seems, then, that both theories, Newton's and Huyghens', told the truth but neither of them the whole truth, a very common case in science as well as on the witness stand. So now physicists are in the queer quandary of having to use both theories, yet are not able to see how they can be reconciled. Sir William Bragg, Professor in the University of London and Nobel Laureate, gave the following witty statement of the situation in "Discovery" of September, 1921:

No known theory can be distorted so as to provide even approximate explanation. There must be some fact of which we are entirely ignorant and whose discovery may revolutionise our views of the relation between waves and ether and matter. For the present we have to work both theories. On Mondays, Wednesdays and Fridays we use the wave theory; on Tuesdays, Thursdays and Saturdays we think in streams of flying energy, quanta or corpuscles. That is, after all, a very proper attitude to take. We can not state the whole truth since we have only partial statements, each covering a portion of the field. When we want to work in any one portion of the field or other, we must take out the right map. Some day we shall piece all the maps together.

The quantum theory (vulgarly known as the "jerk theory") had to be invented when it was found out that radiant energy, such as comes to us in the sunbeams, is not absorbed by the things it falls upon continuously and smoothly, but in certain definite quantities, to be taken in all at a time or none at all; and that these quantities (called "quanta" for short) vary in size according to the frequency of the vibrations of the light they contain. In other words, that light (like oat-meal, nowadays) comes only in packages and you cannot take part of a package. The bigger the package the shorter the wave-length of the light it carrise (though we are rather uncertain what it is that waves). The packages of violet light, for instance, contain nearly twice as much energy as the packages of red light. The X-ray packages are most energetic of all.

Later it was found that a certain quantum of energy would knock out a particular electron from its orbit in the atom, and that this electron would travel off with a speed depending upon the quantum of energy it had received, until it ran into something, when it would deliver up undiminished the quantum of energy that had been imparted to it in the first place. Like a relay race, you understand.

The rule, like all good rules, works both ways. So when an electron, revolving in the outer orbit of the intra-atomic system, falls with a jerk into an orbit nearer the central nucleus, where less energy is required, it sends out its surplus energy with the speed of light in the form of definite quanta of a particular wave-length; and this when it strikes an electron in a similar situation will knock it out of its ring.

It seems, then, that energy can be carried interchangeably in two ways: first, by streams of free flying electrons (as in the cathode rays); and, second, by quanta of radiation (as in the beam of light). Here again I must quote Bragg, because I cannot think up an illustration half so striking as the following:

I drop a log of wood into the sea from a height, let us say, of 100 feet. A wave radiates away from where it falls. Here is the corpuscular radiation producing a wave. The wave spreads, its energy is more and more widely distributed, the ripples get less and less in height. At a short distance away, a few hundred yards perhaps, the effect will apparently have disappeared. If the water were perfectly free from viscosity and there were no other causes to fritter away the energy of the waves, they would travel, let us say, 1,000 miles. By which time the height of the ripples would be, as we can readily imagine, extremely small. Then at some one point on its circumference, the ripple encounters a wooden ship. It may have encountered thousands before that and nothing has happened, but in this one particular case the unexpected happens. One of the ship's timbers suddenly flies up in the air exactly 100 feet, that is to say, if it got clear away from the ship without having to crash through parts of the rigging or something else of the structure. The problem is, where did the energy come from that shot this plank into the air, and why was its velocity so exactly related to that of the plank which was dropped into the water 1000 miles away.

The quantum theory and the relativity theory work together in breaking down the traditional barrier between matter and energy, for the two seem to be in some ways interchangeable. It was discovered in the nineteenth century that one form of energy could be transformed quantitatively into another; for example, machine power into heat and electrical current. It was discovered in the twentieth century that one form of matter could be transformed quantitatively into another, even one element into others, as, for example, radium into helium and lead. It seems now that we

must go further and admit that in certain circumstances
matter may be quantitatively transformed into energy
and the reverse. So that for the two separate laws, the
law of the conservation of mass and the law of the
conservation of energy, we must substitute some single
conservation law that shall embrace them both.

82

HYDROGEN AT WORK

A short cut has been found between the laboratory
and the shop. This is one of the reasons for the amaz-
ingly rapid development of new industries. Take
hydrogen, for instance. Every one who has studied
chemistry will remember hydrogen if he remembers
nothing else, for one of the first experiments he was
set to do was to make hydrogen by dropping bits of
zinc into dilute sulphuric acid. He also remembers
what fun it was to blow soap-bubbles from it and set
them on fire with a taper.

The *ZR-2*, the dirigible that the United States Government bought from England, contained 2,700,000
cubic feet of hydrogen and blew up on her trial trip.
The *Roma* met with the same fate. But science has
overcome this difficulty of the dirigible by substituting
the non-inflammable helium. One day while the conference on the limitation of armament was in session in
Washington a silvery-white cylinder filled with helium
flew over the Pan-American Building, quicker con-
trolled and steadier in flight than a hydrogen balloon.

To the foreign delegates it was a spectacular demonstration of the superior military power of the United States, which has now a virtual monopoly of this rare gas.

But there are more important uses for hydrogen than filling balloon bags. Most extensive of these so far is in the Haber process of fixing nitrogen. In this process nitrogen from the air is combined with hydrogen from water and the two form a new gas, named ammonia. Three tons of hydrogen unite with fourteen tons of nitrogen to make seventeen tons of ammonia.

The awful explosion at Oppau, where thousands of tons of ammonia nitrate prepared for the land blew up, revealed to the world the unparalleled development of this industry in Germany. During the war the allied aviators tried their best to blow up the Oppau works but in vain. Now the Germans have done it for themselves without outside aid, another illustration of the old adage, "If a thing is to be done, do it yourself."

We Americans may console ourselves with the reflection that no such catastrophe can occur in this country, because we have no such plant to blow up!

But although the United States is backward about ammonia, the war gave this country a chance to develop another hydrogen industry of great magnitude—the solidification of oils by the absorption of hydrogen. One would think that the addition of a light gas like hydrogen to a fluid like cotton-seed oil would thin it rather than thicken it. Quite the contrary. The reason oils are oily is because they are short of hydrogen, and when the gas is bubbled through the hot oil in the presence of porous nickel the hydrogen is taken up and the oil solidifies. In this way a light liquid with a rancid

FILLING STAND FOR COMPRESSING OXYGEN OR HYDROGEN

Each cylinder contains 220 cu. ft. of gas at 2000 pounds and at 68 deg. Fah

BANK OF 30 GENERATORS

of the International Oxygen Company for the electrolytic production of oxygen and hydrogen, capacity 4608 cu. ft. of oxygen and 9216 cu. ft. hydrogen per 24 hours.

odor like fish-oil may be transformed into a hard white neutral fat like tallow. Various oils so hydrogenated have come into common use for soap and candles as well as for cooking and table use as a substitute for lard and butter.

The hydrogenation industry is a great and growing one. In the United States alone, millions of cubic feet of hydrogen are consumed every year in the hardening of oils. Probably hydrogen will find further uses of this sort in the production of fuel alcohol and other carbon compounds. The introduction of the tungsten filament lamp has opened a new field for hydrogen, and there are many other opportunities for its employment in metallurgy because hydrogen will take away oxygen from metals and so release them from their ores.

Of course when we need hydrogen by the ton we cannot afford to make it in pint bottles out of zinc and acid as we used to in the laboratory. We must have some way of manufacturing it cheaply and in unlimited quantity. Fortunately the material is abundant and costless. Water contains eleven per cent of hydrogen. The simplest way of separating it from the oxygen to which it is attached is to pass an electric current through the water.

The cheapest way to get hydrogen is to first make water-gas by passing steam over red-hot coke. The oxygen of the water unites with the carbon, forming carbon monoxide, and setting free the hydrogen. Carbon monoxide is a well known fuel gas which in turn breaks up another part of water, freeing its hydrogen and forming carbon dioxide, the ordinary product of combustion.

A third means of producing hydrogen is to pass steam over hot iron in a porous state. The iron abstracts the oxygen from the water and releases the hydrogen. The iron plus the oxygen forms what chemists call the oxide and other people call rust, which can in turn be reduced by carbon monoxide and used again, so that the process alternates continuously and the original iron can be used over and over again.

83

SCIENCE AND RELIGION AS ALLIES

True religion has nothing to fear but much to gain from the scientific study of morality. Ethics is a science, teaching a rational mode of life. Religion is an inspiration to the individual, an aspiration to a high ideal. Science gives eyes to religion. Religion gives a heart to science. Knowledge is power. But power is impotent unless set in action, and dangerous if set in action by the wrong motive. Religion unless guided by knowledge wastes its energies in vague longings or in fruitless and sometimes harmful efforts to reform bodily or social ills.

Throughout the Dark Ages pious people devoted their lives to relieve the sick and suffering, but for lack of medical science they could do little, and often spread the disease they desired to alleviate. Nowadays they can in many cases carry out their pious impulses, for the lepers are cleansed by chaulmugra oil and the lame are made to walk by orthopedics and the blind to see by surgery. Formerly the charitably disposed knew no better than to give alms to beggars. But modern scientific charity shows how the poor can be helped without increasing pauperism. Faith without works is dead.

So are works without faith. The chemist makes picric out of coal-tar. Picric acid is both a healing drug and a high explosive. Whether it is used to kill or to cure depends on how moral man has become. The chemist as a chemist has nothing to say about this, though he may as a citizen. The mechanic makes an automobile but does not know whether it is to be used to carry milk to babies or moonshine to bootleggers.

The public eagerly queries the scientist about whether Mars is habitable but turns a deaf ear when the scientist tries to tell how the earth can be made more habitable. Now, it cannot be expected that science will continue to provide the world with explosives and automobiles without ever having anything to say about how they shall be used. Science will not be content to confine itself to impractical speculations or to the satisfaction of man's material needs and the increase of his wealth. Science is going to have more and more to say about the causes and consequences of conduct. It will point out in what direction the human race may progress. It will discover what conduct is most conducive to human welfare.

But science as such cannot go beyond this. It can point out the best way, but it cannot inspire the individual to follow it against his personal interest. Mere knowledge cannot of itself supply the motive for self-sacrifice for others or for the future. It cannot make a mother risk her life for her child or a man risk his for his country. The altruistic impulse is a religious instinct whether it is recognized as such or not.

The geologist says to the oil prospector, "You will waste half the petroleum if you bore here."

The oil man answers, "What of it if I can make more money now?"

The eugenist says to the infatuated youth, "That girl is no fit mother for your children."

And he answers: "What of it? I want her."

It is useless to urge the interests of posterity for the old retort comes back, "What has posterity ever done for me that I should sacrifice my interests for it?"

The only reply to this is, "I don't know why, but you ought to anyway."

This is a good answer, but it is the answer of religion, not of science. The law may in time prevent the waste of oil and the making of injurious marriages, but it cannot compel the voluntary choice of ethical conduct.

Morality is a matter of individual motive, although the *mores* may be set by the community. Not all sins are social. A man does not need any help to be wicked. *Robinson Crusoe* was deprived by his insulation of the opportunity of committing certain crimes, such as murder and theft, but he had plenty of ways to be wicked when he wanted to. It was a sin for him to get lazy and neglect to weed his garden or to get mad and smash up his furniture.

Sociology, though an immature science, has already done much for religion by pointing out wise methods of altruistic activity. Psychology, a still younger science, promises to do still more for religion by disclosing the emotional motives for our conduct and showing how character can be trained. Every advance of science extends the ability of religion to accomplish its unique aims.

Science can supply motive-power. Religion must supply the motive.

84

SMASHING UP ATOMS

We used to think of atoms—when we thought of them at all—as little round hard things like minute marbles. We had not any reason to suppose them round, but that was the easiest way to think of them. The reason we imagined them hard was that there seemed no possible way to break them up into smaller pieces, and we are accustomed to think of unbreakable things as hard. The very word "atom" meant something that could not be subdivided. The Greek philosophers who invented the term thought that they had reached the ultimate units of which all matter is composed. Modern chemists inherited the idea of the indivisible atom from the ancient Greeks and applied it to the elements that they were not able to decompose. There were some eighty of these elements known, and no one of them could be changed into any other or split up into finer particles.

But now in view of our increasing knowledge we must discard this old crude notion of the atom and think of it as a sort of solar system with a central nucleus around which revolve at enormous speeds one or more lighter bodies called "electrons," as the earth and other planets revolve around the sun.

The nucleus, the sun of the atomic system, is charged with positive electricity. The electrons, on the contrary, are charged with negative electricity, or, we might better say, are atoms of negative electricity. Positive and negative electricities attract each other, and so the electrons are kept from flying the track by the attraction of the positive nucleus as the earth is kept in its orbit by the attraction of the gravitation of the sun.

The reason why we have come to believe that the atom is not a simple and indivisible thing but is made up of these two minute particles, nuclei and electrons, is because we can actually get them out of the atom.

The electron is more easily dislodged than the nucleus because it is much lighter and is on the outside. For illustration, if a big comet came driving through the solar system it would be much more likely to carry off one of the planets, especially the outermost, Neptune or Uranus, than it would to disturb the sun in the center. So, too, we find that the electrons revolving in the outermost orbits of the atomic system can sometimes be knocked off by light or electricity. If a metal is heated to redness it will began to give off electrons Or if a ray of sunlight strikes a metal it will dislodge a few electrons from the outer rings of the atoms. If instead of sunlight the more energetic X-rays strike the plate more electrons will be liberated, some of them even from the inner rings nearest to the nucleus. The atom that has thus been robbed of one or more of its electrons will soon replace them by gathering in any stray electrons that happen to come within reach.

To smash up the nucleus itself is a much more diffi-

FOG TRACKS OF RADIUM PROJECTILES

The alpha particles are ejected from a radioactive atom with a speed of seven or eight thousand miles per second, and when they pass through the nitrogen atoms of the air they detach electrons or even break up the nucleus. Where the track is seen to deflect or divide such a collision has occurred.

Photographs taken by Professor W. D. Harkins, University of Chicago.

cult undertaking than to knock one of its satellite electrons out of the ring. But even this was actually accomplished by Professor Ernest Rutherford of Cambridge University. He did it very ingeniously by bombarding the nucleus with the fragments of other exploding nuclei. The atoms of radium and a few other heavy metals are in an unstable state. A certain proportion of the atoms of radium are breaking up spontaneously all the time, giving off very powerful radiations of three different sorts, partly X-rays, partly streams of negative electrons, partly streams of positive particles. These last are called "alpha particles" on account of the fondness of scientists for talking Greek.

The alpha particles, after they have picked up a couple of electrons apiece, turn out to be ordinary neutral atoms of helium, the lightest of gases next to hydrogen. That is, an alpha particle is the nucleus or central sun of a helium atom. Its size is about one ten trillionth of an inch—if you know how little that is.

But although the alpha particles are so minute they are shot out from the radium atoms at such high speed that they have great penetrating power. They will not only penetrate a metal but actually pass through the atom of the metal. An alpha particle striking a sheet of aluminum may go right through one hundred thousand atoms before it is stopped. About two particles in every million may come into collision with the inner nucleus of the aluminum atoms and knock it to pieces.

Now, when this occurs the pieces of the positive nucleus turn out to be the nuclei of hydrogen. The nucleus of hydrogen starts off with even more energy than the alpha particle which released it, and as it dashes off at high speed among and through the surrounding atoms it snatches from one of them a negative electron and so becomes an ordinary hydrogen atom. That is to say, if we subject a sheet of metallic aluminum to a radium bombardment we shall get from it minute amounts of hydrogen gas.

Here, then, is a case of the direct transmutation of the elements proved by experiment. But it does not stand alone. Professor Rutherford has been able to get hydrogen out of boron, nitrogen, fluorine, sodium, and phosphorus as well as from aluminum. While this work was done in England, it confirmed in a remarkable way a theory of the constitution of atom nuclei propounded four years before in America. At that time Professor Harkins of the University of Chicago developed a hydrogen-helium theory which pointed out specifically that only elements of odd number should give hydrogen by disintegration; and the surprising fact is that the elements listed above as giving hydrogen have numbers 5, 7, 9, 11, 13, and 15, which are all odd numbers. The heavier atoms, such as gold and lead, are not disintegrated, even although their nuclei are probably less stable. This is because, as is well known, positive electricity repels positive electricity. The nuclei of very heavy atoms are charged with a much larger positive charge and thus repel the positively charged alpha particles so greatly that they are not able to approach closely enough to disrupt the heavy atom nucleus.

Neither does oxygen, though it is comparatively light and its positive nuclear charge relatively small, break up under such a bombardment. This is because all of the hydrogen present in it is firmly bound up into alpha particles, four of which, according to the theory, constitute the nucleus of an oxygen atom. Thus, although we have not succeeded in extracting hydrogen out of all the elements, it seems safe to infer that they all have a similar structure and are mostly made up of hydrogen or rather of its nucleus, which seems to be one of the two units of the universe. The negative electron is the other. Four atoms of hydrogen unite to form one atom of helium, the next higher element, and the heavier atoms are all constructed up out of these two building-blocks. For instance, the atom of nitrogen, which weighs 14, is, according to the Harkins theory, composed of three heliums, each weighing four, and two extra hydrogens, which, not being so tightly bound up as those in the triplex helium, can be knocked off. Oxygen weighs 16 and is composed of four heliums and has no loosely attached hydrogens. Carbon weighing 12 is composed of three heliums and no extra hydrogen. That is why no hydrogen is given off from oxygen or carbon. But the aluminum atom weighs 27 and may be built up of six heliums and three outer hydrogens, and this, as we have seen, gives off hydrogen when bombarded by radium.

So this new method of research not only enables us to break up the atom and change one element into another but also promises to give us an insight into the internal structure of the minutest particles in the universe.

85

Laws and Revolutions in Science

In these snap-shots of scientific subjects I have occasionally used the words "law" and "revolution," and since these words are most familiar in their political sense I feel that I should add a word of warning that they mean something quite different in scientific discussions. Both science and religion have suffered from inheriting a misfit legal phraseology that has much embarrassed their growth.

When we talk about a "revolution" in science or of the "overthrow of a law" we are using metaphorical and misleading language. A scientific "revolution" usually leaves the facts and figures in the text-books quite unchanged. The scientist very rarely has to "take back" anything, but he has to keep making over everything.

The carrying over of that unfortunate word "law" from government into science has caused an infinite amount of misunderstanding. "Law" in science does not mean a command or ordinance. Consequently a scientific "law" can never be "disobeyed," "violated," "evaded," "reversed," "suspended," or any of those things. A law in science is simply a description in the fewest possible words of what happens. It is a summary of all that is known on that subject at the time it is formulated.

The confusion has been made worse by including theories and hypotheses under the term "law." A theory or hypothesis is either a law on probation (like a bill before the legislature) or, more often, a mental picture or mechanical model that makes the idea easier to grasp. There is therefore no inconsistency in discarding one hypothesis for a better one, or even in holding two incompatible hypotheses at the same time, if neither alone is adequate, which, as Professor Bragg amusingly shows in the quotation given on page 250, is now the case in regard to theories of light.

When of a morning you look into the magnifying side of your shaving-glass you see a very different face from the one you view in the other side. What seemed a fair smooth cheek in the plain glass is here shown as rough and pitted as the moon seen through a telescope, and your only consolation is that the world does not see what you shave. Now, the scientist holds a mirror up to nature, and it is a magnifying mirror at that. Every new instrument and mathematical device adds to the power of man to look closer, and this puts a new face on things. The new aspect has to be described in new words, not because the old description was wrong, but because it has become inadequate to cover the added knowledge.

There are no laws in nature. What we call the "laws of nature" are the memory schemes we invent to aid us in grasping a lot of facts at one time. When our knowledge is growing rapidly, as it is now, we have to shift to new and larger formulas very suddenly. But this requires stretching the mind to take in bigger ideas, which is as painful a process as stretching an unused muscle. No wonder we tend to dodge it.

INDEX

Acids, 107

Acids in soft drinks, 106

Actresses hissed, 46

Advantages of Tan, 119

Advertising by plants and birds, 26

Agriculture, Inefficiency of, 153

Agriculture, U. S. Department of, 109, 228

Airplanes, 50

Alchemists make rash promises, 24

Alcohol, 141

Alice in Wonderland, 62

Allen, Dr. E. J., 193

American Association for the Advancement of Science, 72

Ancestral Scandals of Science, 23

Anesthetics, 233

Antares, how big he is, 86

Arrhenius, Svante, 42

Astronomy, 210

Athenians say ''Oh!'' 18

Atoms, 41

Aurelian dare not ride in a cart, 46

Australian eclipse observations, 205

Back of Babel, if we can get there, 216

Bacon advises unreasonable experiments, 29

Bacon, Francis, 29, 222

Bacteria, 198

Bananas could not be given away, 47

Bath-tubs legislated against, 47

Bayer 205: what is it worth to world? 203

Benzene, 42, 51

Berthelot, 42

Betelgeuse, how he was measured, 86

Bicephalous calves, 18

Biology in the public press, 151

Birds, how they take up homesteads, 211

Birth-rate, 17

Blood, action of, 155

Body-guard, 155

Bohr, Niels, analyzes the atom, 41

Bone, W. A., 172

Botanic Garden, 185

Bragg, Sir William, 250, 252

Buddha, 146

Byron's Blunders, 82

Caffein in soft drinks, 109

Caldwell, Dr. Otis W., 150

Campbell, President W. W., 205

Can Christians wear trousers? 46

Carbolic acid contributes to a perfume, 38

Carbon dioxide, 91, 107

Carnegie Institution of Washington, 134

Carrel, Dr. Alexis, 156

Carroll, Lewis, not named on page 62

Cassina recommended as a beverage, 108
Castor oil contributes to perfume, 37
Cellulose, 49
Chardonnet, Count de, 49
Chattability of Science, 3
Cheating in nature, 27
Chemical warfare, 36, 197
Chemists should ruin health, 53
Chevreul holds record for longevity among chemists, 54
Chlorophyl, 192
Clements, Dr., 134
Coal supply, 71
Coal thrown away in Philadelphia, 47
Coal-oil from Coal, 230
Coal-tar products, 139
Columbus makes mistake in figuring, 24
Combustion, heat of, 170
Coming social psychologist, 173, 174
Conservation of mass and energy, 70
Consumption remedy from poison gas, 37
Control of life, 157
Corbett, William, fights the potato, 144
Coryate uses a fork, 45
Crazy Experiment and What Came of It, 28
Creevey thought he had stopped locomotives, 44
Crookes, William, 42
Crystallization, 160
Crystals that talk, 8
Cultivation of Obliviousness, 96
Curie, Madame, 126

Dangerous mental malady, 44
Darwin, Charles, 125, 185
Darwin, Erasmus, 185
Death in the Pot, 79
De Morgan, William, 84
Destructive distillation, 30

Diesel engine, 77
Discovery, scientific, 222
Disease, Antiquity of, 127
Do the Papers Lie about Science? 149
Do Two and Two Make Four? 66
Dr. Jekyll and Mr. Hyde, 57
Dodgson, C. L., 62
Domestic animals, 198
Drake, Sir Francis, 143
Dreams, value of, 53, 56
Drugs, synthetic, 197
Dufay, 39
Duisberg, Dr., 220
Dyes, 139

Early Birds, 41
Eclipse and Einstein, 206
Eddington observes eclipse, 127
Ehrlich was called stupid, 202
Einstein, Albert, 43, 68
Einstein in Words of One Syllable, 31
Einstein's Crease, 157
Einstein's prediction verified by eclipse, 206
Electric signs ignored, 97
Electricity, 40
Electricity plus and minus, 40
Electrons, 40
Emily Jane has ten thousand offspring, 16
Endocrinology comes into fashion, 122
Energy, Inventory of, 71
Energy, laws of, 67
Eugenics, 12
Evolution, 125
Experiments of Light better the Experiments of Fruit, 30
Extravagance in nature, 27

Fables are single - barreled weapons, 12
Fagopyrism: Look it up on page 140

Faith of the Scientist, 208
Fake food scares, 78
Faraday, Michael, 131, 222
Faraday's Razors, 214
Fatigue, 167
Fight against the Potato, 143
Fight for the Food and Fuel of the Future, 75
Finley, Charles W., 150
Fireplaces have their advantage, 170
Fischer did better than his father expected, 42, 162
Fleas, 146, 148
Flies deserve death, 148
Flowers that cheat, 27
Forks thought unmannerly, 45
Fourth dimension, 34, 157, 244
Franklin makes a stove, 170
Franklin's Foresight, 38
Freudianism as a fad, 125
From Complexes to Glands, 122
Fuel, 71
Fuel supply needs looking after, 71
Furfural Wants a Job, 227
Futuristic art diagnosed, 101

Galileo, 246
Galton, 246
Galvanism, 82
Gas, illuminating, 82
Gasolene and Alcohol, 141
Geologists Get an Extension of Time, 125
Geology, 125
Germany demanded place in the sun, 76
Giant and dwarf stars, 87
Gilman, Mrs. C. P., 128
Ginger-ale deservedly popular, 110
Give Us Short Names, 151
Glands control temperament, 124
Grandmothers, how to make useful, 85
Great War, 75

Green leaves give us food and fuel, 192
Guiacol, 38

Haber process for fixing nitrogen, 254
Hamilton, how he discovered quaternions, 55
Hares beat lions nowadays, 4
Harkins, Professor W. D., 68, 262
Harvey, E. N., 168
Has Science Reached Its Limit, 130
Heat, laws of, 115
Helium, 66
Henry's law, 93
Hero of Alexandria invents fakes, 24
Herodotus was the historian of his own times, 63
Hess, Dr. A. F., 112
Highways of Knowledge, 178
History not a safe guide now, 63
History, The New, 65
Holmes, Oliver Wendell, 44, 237
Home-Made Rubber, 219
Hormones as agitators, 124
Hot weather alleviated, 106
How a Chemist Tricked His Wife, 98
How Man Got His Shoe, 102
How Old Is Disease? 127
How Scientific Inspiration Comes, 51
How the Chemist Moves the World, 199
How the Other Half of the Plant Lives, 132
How Words Lose Reputation, 175
Howard, Eliot, 219
Huay, 130
Huntington, 173
Hydrogen, 66

Hydrogen at Work, 253
Hypotheses, 265

Ignorance is worse than darkness, 19
Imagination in science, 54
In Defense of Fireplaces, 170
Inefficiency of Agriculture, 153
Injury, Recovery and Death, 136
Insects as carriers of disease, 148
Interferometer used to measure stars, 86
Inventory of Energy, 71
Iron Nerves, 165

Jukes in the rat family, 14

Kekulé's Benzene Ring, 42, 51
Kelvin, Lord, 126
Kindness not wasted even on rats, 13
Kipling, Rudyard, 61
Kropotkin, Prince, 54

Languages, Too Many, 216
Laws and Revolutions in Science, 264
Leather comes high but we have to have it, 22
Le Bel, 43
Let Us Leave Off Living on Leavings, 20
Letters for Literary Ladies, 118
Lick Observatory photographs eclipse, 205
Liebig advised overwork, 53
Light deflected by sun, 206
Light pressure, 88
Lillie, Dr. R. S., 166
Lincoln School, 150
Lindsay, Vachel, 60
Lioness and the Hare, The, 12
Locomotives cause row in Parliament, 44

Luckhardt, Professor A. B., 234
Lustron, 48

Making Medicines Hit the Mark, 195
Making Sunshine Fatal, 138
Malthusianism among hares, 12
Man Afraid of Nothing, 186
Man and the Machine, 180
Man as a Parasite, 20
Mandeville was a liar, 18
Margarin, 98
Mars, 86
Matter, laws of, 67
Mediums and tricksters, 237
Mendel, 127
Mendeléef, D., 41
Meyer-Betz, sunstruck, 139
Michelangelo, 183
Microbes, 129, 146, 156
Monosyllabic relativity, 33
Moodie, Dr. Roy R. L., 128
Moseley determines crystal structure, 41
Mother Goose, revised version, 87
Mount Wilson Observatory, 86
Moving Pictures, 152, 223

Napier, Sir Charles, 45
National Academy of Sciences, 207
Nature's Advertising, 26
Neophobia: have you got it? 44, 83, 100
New-born nationalities, 216
New Light on the Origin of Life, 191
New Path to Oblivion, 233
New World, 5
Newspaper science not so bad as painted, 150
Newton, 4, 43
Nicolson, A. McLean, 9
Nitrates thrown overboard, 47

Opposition to novelties, 44
Origin of Life, 191, 194
Osterhout, J. V., 135
Ostwald, Wilhelm, 166
Our Domestic Enemies, 146

Paleopathology, 128
Paper, 200
Paracelsus Is Bombast, 24
Parmentier introduced potato, 144
Pasteur, Louis, 42
Paton, Dr. Stewart, 101
Pearl, Professor Raymond, 247
Percentage Aliveness, 135
Perfumes from Poison Gas, 34
Perkin, Sir William, 42, 220
Petroleum, 71, 74, 233
Phagocytes are useful, 155
Phenol products, 233
Philosophy, 245
Phonograph, 15
Phosgene makes perfume, 37
Phosphates as stimulants, 107
Photosynthesis, 155
Pi may not be what it seems, 33
Piezo-electricity: if you don't know what it is see page 10
Plague, 146
Plato, 176
Pliny advocates sun-baths, 111
Plotnikoff, 220
Plumbing opposed by Seneca, 45
Pogoniastic ladies, 18
Poincaré; how his bright ideas came to him, 4
Poison gas makes dyes and drugs, 37
Ponce de Leon is misled in going to Florida, 24
Popover Stars, 84
Potatoes dangerous to society, 47, 144
Priestly discovered oxygen, 186
Printing a chemical art, 200
Printing sneered at, 47

Prophecies, scientific and unscientific, 84
Prout's hypothesis, 66
Psychoanalysis, 123
Psychologists must look out, 174
Pythagoras sacrifices a hundred oxen, 24

Quaker rats, 17
Quantum Theory, 248
Quaternions, Discovery of, 55

Radiant Energy, 72, 89
Radiation, 72
Radium, 261
Rats fond of good music, 13
Red giants do not amount to much, 86
Refrigeration, influence on history, 76
Relativity, Theory of, 31
Religion, 256
Rendezvous, 209
Rewarded for working inside the atom, 41
Rickets cured by sunshine, 112
Robinson agrees with the walrus, 65
Rochelle salt sings a song, 10
Röntgen discovers X-rays, 31
Rollier sets up solarium, 113
Roots go deep, 135
Roscoe, Sir Henry, 164
Rubber, 88
Rumford makes potato-soup, 145
Rutherford, Sir Ernest, 70

Saxe, J. G., on ancestor-worship, 23
Scandals of Science, 23
Scholar in Overalls, 224
Science and Method, 54
Science and Religion as Allies, 256
Science begins in wonder, 17

Science contributions to common life, 200, 224

Science from the Side-Lines, 168

Science gives before she is asked, 222

Science of keeping cool, 114

Science remaking the world, 6

Science scares some folks, 78

Science Service, 5

Scientific Factors in History, 62

Scientific inspiration; how it comes, 51

Scientific theories, 210, 264

Scott, Sir Walter, laughs at gas, 83

Seneca opposes sky-scrapers, 45

Seven C's, 78

Shark-Towed Submarines, 184

Shoes cause killings, 122

Signs of Sanity, 101

Silkworm's Rival, 48

Singing Crystal, 8

Sleeping-sickness devastates Africa, 202

Smashing Up Atoms, 259

Smith, Edgar Fahs, 118

Socrates, 174

Soda-Water, 90

Soft-drinks; what they are made of, 106

Solar energy, 72, 74

Space and Time, 241

Spaeth, Dr. R. A., 165

Spectacles pronounced immoral, 46

Spiritualism, 237

Spoehr, H. A., 154

Stars, Composition of, 87

Stars: how they keep up, 85

Star photographs confirm Einstein, 206

Steam-Engines, Opposition to, 45

Steinach, 124

Stevenson got plots from dreams, 56

Subconscious contributions to science, 53

Success of a Failure, 162

Sugar, 107, 163

Sully-Prudhomme's Sonnet, 209

Summer Drinks, 106

Sun is late yellow dwarf, 89

Sun-cure, 110

Sunshine, 111, 119, 138

Super-Rats, 13

Superstition, 190

Switchel, out of fashion but tasted good, 108

Synthetic shoes needed, 22

Synthetic silk; more of it used than you think, 48

Tan, advantages of, 119

Tangling Up the Time Line, 240

Tappeiner, Herman von, 138

Temperature of stars, 89

Territory: birds fight for it, 211

Territorial Wars of Birds, 211

Thompson, Benjamin, 145

Thomson, J. Arthur, 179

Thomson, J. J., 249

Time, conception of, 240

To Exchange: a Chemical for a Colony, 201

Tomatoes injurious to morals, 47

Tractors, 83

Translating Einstein, 243

Tropics, Value of, 77

Trypanosomes, 202

Tuberculosis, 110

Tut-ankh-Amen was sun worshiper, 110

Tyndall on the imagination, 54

Tyrian purple from a snail, 21

Ultra-Violet Rays, 120, 220

Vaccination, 82

Van't Hoff gets laughed at, 43

Venus, 187

Viscose, 48

Vitamins in soft drinks, 106, 109
Violet perfume from phosgene, 37
Voronov, 124

Wallal Eclipse Observations, 205
Walrus was right, 63
War of Land and Sea, 58
Washington Academy of Sciences hears crystals sing, 8
Water, 58
Water-power, 71
Wave theory of light, 68
Wealth from Science, 225
Weaver, Professor John E., 134
Wells, H. G., 15, 74, 188

Weyl, 241
What Is the Matter with the Artists? 100
Which Organ Will You Give Way First? 247
Wistar Institute, 16
Women as Chemists, 117
Women Players Cause Riot, 46
Wonders of science a passing phase, 17
Wood's Hole, 135, 165
Wool-gathering is humiliating, 22

Yellow journal science, 78

Zoroastrianism, 148